CW00546084

teen poets

Riding Life's Roller Coaster

Edited by Claire Tupholme

First published in Great Britain in 2003 by
YOUNG WRITERS
Remus House,
Coltsfoot Drive,
Peterborough, PE2 9JX
Telephone (01733) 890066

HB ISBN 0 75434 122 4
SB ISBN 0 75434 123 2

Foreword

As part of our ongoing pursuit to present a showcase of today's best up-and-coming authors, Young Writers is now proud to present its 'Teen Poets' series.

Few periods in life are more turbulent - or more crucial in human development than in the early teens. The struggles and trials faced daily can shape and mould our developing persona as we take a tentative step towards our early adult lives. The 'Teen Poets' series aims to bring these growing tribulations to light, providing a valuable snapshot into the thoughts and poetic visions of the teenage mind.

Riding Life's Roller Coaster offers a selection of these poems, as the young writers within tackle a range of vital issues whilst also sharing with us the lighter side of teenage life. The result is a valuable and stimulating insight into the mind-set of the modern youth, and a challenging read for many years to come.

CONTENTS

The Poems

THE WAY I'M FEELING

Can I make you see it from my point of view?
Can I make you want a world with love and peace?
Can I make you see the world your children will grow up in?

Stop the violence, low self-esteem and suicide,
Nobody cares, can you make them care?
Can I make you feel the way I'm feeling?

Can I make you want exactly what I want?
Can I make you see the world we share?
Can I make you understand the problems with society?

I want the world to have meaning,
Just like my life has meaning now that you're here,
Can you help me?
Will you help me make a better world?

Emma Harvey (14)

SILENCE

What is silence?
Is it here or there?
Silence
I can't see it anywhere!
Does it fill the room
Or just a small part?
Is it inside of me?
Is it in my heart?
Even though,
You can't see it,
It is there
Cleverly masked
By its disguise.

Ashleigh-Marie Pickett (13)

The Hunt

Up bright and early, dressed and eager to go
Today is the hunt, more challenging than a show
The saddle is squeaky clean and bridle's gleaming too
The white numhah is in the wash so the navy one will do.
Houdini is exquisite, her plaits are all in line
Her white coat is shining, she looks mighty fine.
The trailer has now arrived, I hope she goes on with ease
We are running out of time now, 'Come on Houdini please.'
The journey has gone quite smoothly, we have now just arrived
Houdini has come off the box, clean and has survived.
Now perched on the saddle, ready to go
The rest of the hunt are waiting, can't be slow!
Of all the jackets the master's red jacket stands out from the rest
Horses and ponies of breeds galore but Houdini really just is the best.
The hounds are off - the hunt has begun
The season is winter so now there's no sun.
The hounds detect a scent and suddenly are gone
We are lead to the first jump, I close my eyes and hold on.
I have completed the first task, full of pride
But I couldn't have done it without Houdini's good stride.
I face them all, hedges, ditches, banks and logs
Until the day is done and tired are all the riders, horses and dogs.
We put the horses away after working with skill
All into the barn to have a drink, chat and chill.
It's getting late so we all must leave
Take the horses back home to relax and breathe.
The day is over I shed a tear
Go to sleep and dream about next year!

Hannah Taylor (13)

There Was Something About Being A Kid

There was something about being a kid
That was so secure,
You went along with what you got
And never asked for more.
You didn't have the answers,
And that was okay
You accepted the present,
It didn't get in your way.
You didn't think for the future
It didn't matter at all
Nobody had expectations,
Life was a ball.
You ate ice cream with your fingers,
Got paint in your hair,
You ran through the sprinklers,
You just didn't care.
But growing up, moving on,
Making you the person you are,
Gaining experience, learning new things,
Moving fast, getting far,
Achieving your dreams,
All through the years
Pushing yourself to the limit,
Confronting your fears,
Sometimes you will fall,
But that's how you grow,
You change and you learn
You work hard and it will show.

Rebecca Tresman (14)

My House

I pull up in my car to the biggest house I have ever seen before
Wondering what it would be like to live there.
I think of all the things I could do to this,
To make it my own dream world.
I would have bright, vibrant colours on the walls
With pretty things all around.
In my garden I would get my family to help me make it look special
People would stop just to look at what my front garden looks like
As it looks so nice it would be my own little world
Where birds would come and sing.
I would have a pond with lots of fish and a big tree
Where I would sit under on a bench
And think of what a great place I live in . . .

My dream house.

Zoé Hewkin (14)

Life As A Teen

L ive life to the full
I f you want to go far
F reedom will come
E veryone must be free of their parents some day.

A nd everyone thinks they know you
S urely they don't think they do?

A nd as if they would!

T he life each one of us leads is different
E veryone needs to be different
E veryone needs to be
N ever mind what anyone says!

Emma Cundall (15)

War

Why is there war?
Why is there hate?
Why cannot we get along
And try to be good mates?

Why hate someone for their skin,
Their opinions or their views?
What matters is what is within
Not skin or thoughts, those things.

So do your bit today and try,
To smile at people as they pass by,
Say, 'Hello!', 'Good morning!', 'Hi!'

Because if we are all friends,
Then all the wars will end.

Elizabeth Robinson (13)

Love

Satin snow and crystal frost,
Winter morning, sun so soft.

Bright, blue skies with fluffy clouds,
The sound of a heart beating very loud.

The sweet smell of grass and fragrant flowers.
This feeling could go on for hours and hours.

A moonlit walk hand in hand,
The summer sun beating down on sand.

The fresh smell of strawberries, a blazing red flame,
The soft, gentle touch of a warm summer's rain.

Abbey Krause (15)

TEENAGE YEARS

Most enjoyable, teenage years,
I don't think so!
No one said about the heartache, hurt and tears,
But I guess they wouldn't, would they?
Though some times are cool,
Like going out with mates and lads.
But other times like school,
They are just so boring.
Parents are so understanding, right?
Put up with our mood swings on top of other stuff.
But why don't we get to stay out late at night?
I guess we're not 'mature' enough.
There are things like alcohol and drugs,
But nasty is their name.
They just turn people into thugs,
Which is nothing anyone wants.
Teenagers stealing cars,
And they think it's fun.
You would think they lived on Mars,
Maybe it would be better if they did.
All the advice that I would give to teenagers to be,
Is always look out for yourself.
Don't rely on friends at all times,
As sometimes they are not all what you see.
So take my advice and be aware of your surroundings!

Victoria Ross (14)

WHO KNOWS?

Today I'm stress free,
That's how I like it to be.

But tomorrow's another day,
I'll try to put my problems away.

This week I might be in a mood,
Then again I could be a totally cool dude.

If by chance my tears should fall,
I'll have to give my best friend a call!

Jemma Brown (13)

HOLIDAY ROMANCE

I arrived on Saturday,
So far things were okay.
Then I saw you sitting across the way,
You winked at me,
You made my day.
Sunday came and so did you,
There's only one thing I could think of
That I wanted to do.
Monday was fantastic you'd waved at me,
I looked at my brother then shouted with glee,
I finally realised it was meant to be.
Tuesday was better, we began to talk,
You invited me to come on a walk.
Wednesday we got together,
And promised each other this love was forever.
Thursday was fab, we shared our first kiss,
I felt like I was in heaven,
It was pure bliss.
When Friday came so did my tears,
Today was worse than facing my fears.
Saturday rolled round,
And I was homeward bound.
Last night you asked for me to dance,
And so this ended my holiday romance.

Hayley Elcock (15)

THE COCOON OF A TEENAGER

A tidal wave of emotion, a pharmacy of hormones,
Half a dozen highs, a library of lows,
Enough anger, depression and hatred to start a world war,
Enough loneliness and anxiety to last a decade,
It knows everything, yet its knowledge is so small,
Half child, half adult and a bit of something else
Too young to be respected, too old to be blameless,
Life is so big and they are so small.

Yet, out of this spotty, fat, complicated cocoon,
Blossoms an incredible individual.

Its life is full of laughter
Every day contains some happiness
The mirror reflects beauty
And clothes complement its figure.
People are attracted to its friendly exterior
Friends become close because of its unique interior
Goals are set, the future looks bright
And from inside there flows a peace, a peace not of this world
A peace that will remain for eternity.

Charlotte Wright (14)

THE WORLD

The world is a strange place, colourless and dull
If I were in control I'd surely pull
Pull our world away from poverty and pain
In my eyes it's religion that is to blame.

Do you honestly believe just one man
Can do all the things he claims he can?
Change water to wine, stone to bread
Ride on a cloud to Heaven when he's dead.

If for one moment we could forget religion
Which causes pain and countries collision
Even forget about our nationality
We'd be free to concentrate on reality.

Joe Foster (13)

FAVOURITISM

She's obviously the favourite
It's so unfair.
She thinks I don't notice
But she doesn't care.
We're more than one
There's three of us
She picks out one
And makes a fuss.
When the two of us confront her
She thinks it's all a joke
What's the point in trying?
She'll just give us a poke!
We just get angry,
We lash out fast,
We aim to destroy,
But it doesn't last.
My father steps in
And takes control
We ask him why
He says it's his role.
I know that she's the favourite
Why? Oh why?
Was I cursed with this sister
And this mother of mine?

Mair Jeffreys (14)

Norwich

Norwich hasn't changed a lot
It still has its most important plots.
The mall, cathedral and the museum too
Let me think what else has Norwich got?
Shopping, football and racing too.
A lot of things for kids to do.
Arcades and parks are what they have
So let's get going.

Norwich is big and bright
It has a good night life.
Clubbing, pubbing or sitting down
We have the best all around.
Ikon, Time or The Loft
Some of the places you could stop.

Norwich is for all ages
Doesn't mater if you're old or young
You can still have fun
You could be one or fifty
It doesn't matter
Just come along.

Nikki Wilby (14)

My Room

Dirty socks,
Mouldy cheese,
Muddy shoes,
Smelly jeans,
Dusty shelves,
Mucky doors,
Greasy walls.

Clean socks,
Binned cheese,
Shiny shoes,
Fresh jeans,
Polished shelves,
Pristine doors,
Smooth walls.

Louise Brockbank (13)

BETRAYAL

Crystal glass glistens in the morning light.
Memories of old, childhood fantasies,
Embossed with the colour of dreams.
Photographs of us together
As we once were,
Sharing smiles of friendship.

But then the smile faded.
Your face, now distorted with evil.
The bond between us destroyed
Darkness lurked in those familiar eyes,
Which I once gazed into with affection.
You waited to pierce my heart,
Until it was completely destroyed.

Anger surges through my body
When I think of what you did,
The people you hurt, the lies you told.
Hand tremble,
Gripping the picture frame,
Broken glass.
Shattered fragments of memories
Betrayed.

Anna-Marie Smith (15)

A Night Poem

It's Sunday and it's the dead of night
Half the Earth is bathed in moonlight.

Now no human is awake,
Retired to bed for resting's sake.

At this time dill and bindwort flower,
For it is . . . the witching hour.

Things mundane, the shrew, the bat,
Are creeping when the moon is fat.

And over the dustbins, over the roof,
The agile feline is quite aloof.

But let's step away from the usual
To a place of enchantment, magical.

Journey to the forest's secret glen,
A sanctuary from the hands of men.

On the rock sits a mermaid, like a jewel
In the centre of the silvery pool.

Beautiful, with face so fair,
With emerald tail and flowing hair.

But to think she was virtuous you would be wrong,
For many have drowned to the sound of her song.

. . . Subsequeous, waterbound mermaid,
Is not alone in this green glade . . .

Come creatures which retreat at dawn
The griffin and the unicorn.

To partake in bewitching dance,
Until next nightfall, their last chance.

Then the moon is covered by a cloud,
That for the while will be its shroud.

And the night-being's hark
All are plunged into the dark.

Kate Duffield (13)

THOSE EYES

I'm standing, staring in the mirror
My face looks dull and bleak
Those insane eyes scan the figure
Of that person, oh so weak.

In school I'm busy all day long
No time for hurt or pain
Yet the minute I walk through the gates
Those eyes sear through my head again.

My friends all live so far away
The telephone doesn't ring
The cloudy, grey sky towering tall
Gives me no song to sing.

Happiness comes when I go out
Shopping with my mates
Laughter quickly envelops the tears
I forget troubles and hates.

I'll never believe the person in me
I'll never expect clear skies
I'll always be haunted in my dreams
Because I'll always see those eyes.

Leanne Thompson (14)

FRIENDS

Friends, mates, pals, buddies;
Whatever you may call them
They always are: people you like,
You trust and know really well.
Most of my friends are girls my age,
But some are boys
And some are older or younger than me,
But however old they may be
They're still my friends.
My friends and I laugh together,
Talk together and sit together at school
But we don't do everything together.
We arrange sleepovers,
Shopping and cinema trips,
And a day away ice skating.
Sometimes we fall out,
But we always make up again
Because friends are forever.

Edith Knox (13)

MY SECRET

I used to have a secret
Which I told my bestest friend,
I knew that I could trust her
Until the very end.

Then the secret slipped
And spread throughout the school,
Every year group laughed at me
I was named the fool.

The friendship was soon over
She's standing at my door
I won't answer it though,
We don't talk anymore.

Bethany Palumbo (14)

SEPTEMBER 11TH

Plane crashed in Twin Towers
They say it was a terrorist attack
It was there, they buried their flowers
Innocent people dying with their families crying.

They called their loved ones
'Cause they knew what was happening
They wanted to call them before their lives were done
Innocent people dying with their families crying.

They blame it on Bin Laden
For the terrorist attack
Why did he have to cause this bombardment?
Innocent people dying with their families crying.

Bin Laden is in hiding
No one knows where he is
People looking but never finding
Innocent people dying with their families crying.

We'll soon have to find him
'Cause there's helicopters going round
Everything is looking gloomy and dim
Innocent people dying with their families crying.

Louisa Graver (13)

My Room

According to the colour chart,
The colour of my room has the characteristic fresh,
But it can be anything.

After a hard day at school
It's soothing, relaxing and tranquil and so is the music
But when I'm lively, the room is too with a buzzing electric atmosphere
When my mind wanders, my room is like an open expanse of sea
To explore and delve in.
As my eyelids close, it's humble, drifting me off to sleep.

My room is my sanctuary,
But like no other,
Like a person, it has different sides,
My room does too.

I can see why the colour chart says it's fresh
But why not give it another characteristic,
Other than fresh?
Oh, I forgot to tell you the colour of my room - it's aqua pool.

Stephanie Morris (13)

Snowy

She flutters in the moonlight,
Her wings sparkling silvery white.

Her eyes shining ever so bright
As she flies, flies into the night.

Hunting, watching for little mice,
Remembering how they taste so nice.

Waiting, longing for a wonderful slice,
She flies, flies into the night.

As the sun is rising in the sky
It's time for Snowy to say goodbye.

She flies, flies into the night,
Before it becomes broad daylight.

Ayeshea Taylor (13)

Loneliness

Together or in isolation
What's the difference? What's the point?
Surrounded by people
Family or friends
Yet: empty in such hollow thoughts,
No longer wanting to live
Surrounded by people
And still, it makes you feel lonely like being in an empty room.
Not one living creature who breathes
The same air as you.

Until one morning you awaken
Only to realise that to be lonely is to live
In depression, confusion, isolation.

It is to be lonely
Togetherness is how the world works
A step forward in the world
It is how we make the world go round.

Sabina Ahmed (13)

What Has Become Of This World?

(Dedicated to Holly Wells and Jessica Chapman.)

We are the master race
Yet still we act without a moment of thought.
Self involvement and gratification
Is what drives us on day after day.
The feelings and the consequences evict sane thinking,
Leaving evil to do its worst.

But those of us that resist, sit helpless
Addicted to the hope that others will prevail.
Yet those whose hope you're addicted to - keep stumbling,
Just a little out of their reach - is the solving and destroying of evil.

If those of us sitting helpless,
Wake from the slumber and look within
They would find that they hold the key.
Just analyse the world and its society that surrounds you
Yet the answer that you are presented with, is not the one you sought
You are still left with one question

What has become of this world?

Dale Charlton (15)

When Love Dies

Love is a treat
Only you can feel the heat
The warmth and security
Peace and purity.

Pain overflows
As my love grows
Oh how I try
Not to cry.

I want you near me
It's only you I see
When I close my eyes
It hurts when love dies.

Charlotte Page (14)

WHY SHOULD I CHANGE?

I am who I am
I will not change me
This is how I've been created,
What you get is what you see,
This is how God has made me,
Either you like it or you don't.
You can try your best to change me
But believe me you won't.
I will stay who I am
Whether you like it or not,
You can make a plan against me
You can even make a plot,
But I won't stop,
Being who I am.
Maybe one day,
You will learn to understand,
Never judge a book by its cover,
If you take a deeper look
You don't know what you might discover,
So next time,
Think before you hate,
You might hate the wrong person
Don't make that big mistake.

Phoebe Raphael (14)

ANGELA

My friend's mum's life came to an end
When her body got taken over
By the dreaded cancer that kills hundreds ever year.
At the age of forty-two
Her life got stolen
And she left a loving family behind.
I do not look back in grief
But with a great bundle of happiness
'Love Is All Around' was her favourite song
And every time I hear it I can't help but think of her.
I went to the funeral with my mum
And saw my friend with her family and expected Angela to follow.
I couldn't get it in my head that she wasn't coming back.
Laura, my friend did not cry in my presence
But I knew that she hurt inside.
I hope that a cure can soon be found
So no one has to experience what Angela,
Her family and we had to go through.
Angela may be gone but her spirit is still alive,
And always will be.

Lauren Glidden (14)

MY LITTLE KITTEN

I have a little kitten
His name is Mitten,
I am just smitten,
To have a little kitten.

I have a little dog,
His name is Bob,
He is such a little dog,
My dog Bob.

I have a little fish,
His name is Splish,
It's just so bliss
To have a fish.

Aimée Skillen (14)

WHEN I AM THIRTY . . .

When I am thirty I might be . . .
A sailor, sailing out to sea.
When I am thirty I might be . . .
A stewardess serving tea.
When I am thirty I might be . . .
A teacher, teaching ABC.

When I am thirty cool I'll be
Everyone will look at me
'Wow!' They'll say, 'What a star
Cruising round in that cool car.'

When I am thirty happy I'll be
And my favourite star won't be Britney.
When I am thirty I'll no longer play
I'll sit at a desk doing work all day.

When I am thirty I might be . . .
A sailor, sailing out to sea.
When I am thirty I might be . . .
A stewardess serving tea.
When I am thirty I might be . . .
A teacher, teaching ABC.

Lois Harries (13)

My World

I look around me and what do I see?
A world full of hatred spread before me,
The creation of new life, destruction of old,
A life of misery begins to unfold.

Third world poverty resulting in death,
Why do we allow such a terrible mess?
With world debt repayments towering high,
People left starving, many soon die.

Twin Towers, once magnificent came tumbling down,
The ashes of disaster lay scattered on the ground,
As the world so defenceless looked on in dismay,
September 11th what a terrible day!

Illness, disease, hunger and more,
Quality of life for some is so poor,
Hopes for the future, regrets from the past,
With help they'd find happiness that surely would last.

We are the new generation,
Our voices soon will be heard,
But right now big changes need to be made,
Or a heavy price will soon have to be paid.

I look around me and what do I see?
A world full of hatred spread before me,
The creation of new life, destruction of old,
A life of misery begins to unfold.

Caroline Tully (15)

THE PERFECT PLACE

I dream I find a perfect place
A perfect place somewhere,
The glory of Heaven has overflowed,
And from the sky has descended to there.

As the sun's tranquil rays shine down,
Bathing the land in gold,
Ripples of perfect beauty,
Flow from inside its soul.

Mists swirl through the dawn,
As crystal raindrops fall,
Cobwebs stretch adorned,
With necklaces of jewels.

Flowers elegantly pose,
Their colours painting the darkness of night,
As beautiful melodies arise from the dawn,
Sweet aromas scent the twilight.

Streams bubble and dance through the mist,
Their waters whispering in shimmering pools,
Ripples adorn its sparkling surface,
As the waters deluge in glistening waterfalls.

So every night when I lay in slumber,
Asleep by those shimmering streams,
When darkness throws its cloak over me,
I can enlighten it with my dreams.

Amy Forshaw (13)

Be You And Be Proud

It's not what's on the outside, it's what's on the inside.
It's not what language you speak, it's what you say.
It's not what colour you are, it's who you are.
Never try to change yourself for someone else,
Be you and be proud!

You may look different but you're just the same
Your heart is beating again and again
Never let someone put you down
Be you and be proud!

You may get picked on because of the way you look,
But they don't realise they're not perfect either
Never judge a book by its cover
Be you and be proud!

Charlotte Skillen (14)

Friends

Goodbye old friend, it's time to go
But before you leave I want you to know
If I go to Heaven before you do
I'm going to sit up there and wait for you.
'Cause you're my friend, that you already know
But I really don't want you to go.

The sky is grey now you have left,
I really do just want the best.
But . . .
Life is hard without a friend
To be there for you until the end . . .

Natalie McQueen (13)

SEASONS

Winter
Frost freezes,
Snow falls,
Rain splashes,
Wind crawls.

Spring
New things,
Daffodils everywhere,
New beginnings,
The new, clean, fresh air.

Summer
Sun sets in,
Rain sets out,
No more rain,
No more drought.

Autumn
Back comes rain,
Away goes sun,
Here comes cold
No more fun.

Seasons
Seasons come and go
The summer sun,
The winter rain,
Seasons come and go.

Daniel Sharp (12)

THIS SIDE OF ME

I've lived my life as someone else,
I wanted to determine who I was
But my identity remains a mystery
You made me think I was someone who I'm not
I sit here now as someone time forgot
You made me believe I was wrong
Inside I was weak
Outside you were strong
I was no match for you and all that hurt you put me through.

I reflect upon my life
Painful memories of a wasted existence
I look at us now and I see a huge difference
You've lived this lie with no doubts or fear
But I tried to fight as the end drew near.
Everyone in this place is so tried, everything's fake
Nothing is true
I made the mistake of listening to you.

You've never seen this side of me
Now you catch a glimpse of who I can be.
You've seen inside my head
My thoughts are immortal,
My heart and soul is their mystic portal.

I've finally revealed this side of me
You can't push me around any more
I'm finally free.

Shelley Piluke (14)

My Perfect World

I think, I think what the world would be
Without any wars or enemies.
Without any hatred, evil or fear
Or wondering hopelessly if death is near.
Without any racism, prejudice or slavery
Or hearing people scream 'Oh save me.'
No bullying or fighting within schools,
No truanting, rudeness or breaking the rules.
No need for running from an untimely death
No terrorism, vandalism, raping or theft.

Only kindness, happiness and love,
And peace and faith sent from above.
All people living happily as never before,
All having a huge, big smile when they open the door.
White, half-caste, black or even blue
Should all be treated, as they want to
This would be my perfect world
As you see from what I've told.
Earth should be a place of peace
Well that's what I think but I'm only me.

Lauren Welch (13)

Happiness

Happiness is pink.
It tastes like marshmallows
And smells like candyfloss.
Happiness looks like pink hearts
And sounds like happy music.
Happiness is warm.

Laura Millar (13)

Mylo

Floppy ears,
Wet nose,
Big feet,
Padded toes.

Brown eyes,
Black spots,
Four little
White socks.

Long tail,
White chest,
This is the dog,
I love the best!

My dog Mylo!

Amy Wiffen (13)

It

It is still there, but I do not see
But then again, does it see me?
Does it whistle through the trees?
Does it sail the seven seas?
Is it the voice deep inside?
Does it scare me? Shall I hide?
What shall I do? Where shall I go?
Does it even know, I know?
Is it young or is it old?
No, it is not there, I did not see
It does not whistle . . .
    It's only me!

Victoria Roach (13)

Love Poem

Love is like two newly weds,
Love can make you light in the head,
Love can be a wonderful thing,
It makes my heart go ring, ring, ring.
Love is such a gentle thing
When it touches your heart and stays within.
Love is such a powerful thing
Some people think of it as a sin.
Love is like being in a dream
Like eating strawberries and cream.
Love sounds like the song of a bird
Which only this morning I heard.
Love stays with you all your life
Through everything including strife.

Danielle Welsh (13)

The Bully

Every day on my way home
Constantly looking over my shoulder
They take everything, opportunity, self-confidence,
Even my warmth, gone, I am left to grow colder and colder
No conscience, no guilt, no second thought,
They just don't care about the misery they have brought
My life is stuck on a loop
Out of which I fear I will never escape.
Me against their group
So exclusive nobody knows
Yet still it happens
Every day on my way home.

Rachel Watchorn (14)

THE MIRROR DOESN'T LIE

It stands there, a monster of the truth
No matter where you turn it always sees and always shows.
Your eyes fix on the criticism of your image
That is you!
This is what everyone else sees.
Sharp eyes look at you in the street,
Whispers behind your back
And you stand in front of the mirror
What is wrong?
Why am I like this?
But you still stand.
You watch and wait, seeing if you'll change
Will you be the duckling that changes to a swan?
But all that time you hear the whispers and giggles
The mirror never lies.

Kathryn Osland (15)

MY MUM IS THE BEST

My mum is the best
She is better than all the rest
She feeds me every single day
And when I'm bored she comes out to play.
When I'm ill or have a cut
She's always there to cheer me up
And when the birds are singing
In their pretty nests
I always think of my mum
Because she is the best!

Anna Davies (13)

GIRL GUIDE CAMP

It's that time of year again
The guider says,
'I've recovered from last year
Let's do it again.'
Some frown, others laugh
Signing up for guide camp.

The date draws near
The canvas comes out
How do I make bedding roll?
I can't remember!

We all arrive and the pitching starts
Grab a mallet and a peg
Stand correctly or get a smack!

Share the duties in patrols
Do we need to teach you how to wash up?
There's no dishwasher here!

The points are collected
Which patrol will win?
Who gains the most points for going to sleep?

The week draws to a close
The guiders celebrate
We all enjoy a sing-song round the campfire.

The tents come down,
The cup awarded,
The girls look exhausted.

Everyone says goodbye and leaves
That is until next year.

Kelly James (15)

WHAT IS LOVE?

What is love? That's a good question
I don't know what love is
I don't think anyone truly knows what love is.
Does the giddy schoolgirl with her boyfriend
Holding hands in the park,
Kissing at the school discos
Does she know what love is?
What about the student, going to parties and hanging with his mates
He spends every day talking to his girlfriend back home
Does he miss her and wish he could be with her?
Does he know what love is?
The divorced woman, left by her husband to raise two kids
Would she have married him
If she'd known it was going to end like this?
Does she know what love is?
Then there's the old lady, her husband's just died
They spent the whole of their lives together
Sharing each other's experiences, living each day as it came
Never knowing what was going to happen,
Never caring
Just knowing they were together was all that mattered
Did they know what love is?
To know, you have to love
And to love you have to go through so much for one person.
You have to leave your life in their hands
To trust them to never lead you astray
To know that one day
That person may not be with you any more in life
But that they will still be with you in soul
For ever, eternity
Do you know what love is?

Becky Whing (15)

Loved And Lost

She ran through moors, her clothes in rags,
Tears streaming from her eyes.
How could she have believed his words?
His angry shouts and cries.

She felt so lonely, hurt and sad,
He wasn't true to her.
He didn't return home one night
She was under pressure.

She ran and ran through thick brambles,
Her smooth skin ripped to shreds.
She should have been prepared for this,
Though they were newly weds.

She just sat down to rest a while,
Her breath a short, sharp gasp.
For she was trapped, so cold and hard,
In his cruel, evil grasp.

She tried to break free many times,
But he was much stronger
If he got his way she wouldn't
Be here for much longer.

She was, by now, so cold and weak;
She had been dragged for miles.
Her hair hung limp like threads of string,
He was so mean and vile.

She couldn't move she was so cold,
He'd scared her to the bone.
It was his fault she ran away,
She'd heard him on the phone.

Alice Shellock (14)

THE GARDEN OF FOUR SEASONS

Gardens are packed with millions of flowers,
In summer they're filled with beautiful colours.
The smell of the flowers that I breathe,
The sight of the butterflies that I see,
The sound of the birds twittering in the tree,
I take it all in happily with glee.

Leaves come in all shades: red, yellow, brown and gold,
It's the same autumn, but it'll never get old,
They make a soft blanket on the ground,
So that you can tread without a sound.
The clouds become heavy and grey with rain,
Then droplets trickle down my windowpane.

In the winter the garden is frozen over,
The grass coloured like the White Cliffs of Dover,
The evergreens slightly sprinkled with snow
The ferns come to life as the wind does blow
The apple tree like a picture postcard,
The ice on the pond, rock hard.

In the blaze of the summer's sun,
How I wished that winter had begun,
But now I know, I would much rather go
To spring, when all plants start to grow.
The blossoms from the apple tree fall
To replace my snow; I have it all.

The summer is hot, the winter is cold,
In spring it's fresh, in autumn it's gold,
The seasons mean we cannot escape
The garden's ever changing landscape.
Every year the seasons come,
And in every one I have fun.

Natalya Palit (13)

A Message To Parents - Please Understand

Banging music and slamming doors
Sex, drugs and breaking laws,
We really don't all live this way
All we want is to have our say.

We're crying out to be heard
To just ignore us would be absurd
We're desperate for you to understand
Don't bury your head beneath the sand.

We shout, we snap and we cry
Some of us even cheat and lie
But please don't just go in a huff
Being a teenager is really tough.

Exams, careers and dreaded school
Doing our best to try and look cool
Boyfriends and things we shouldn't do
And then of course, there's pleasing you.

Our hearts will be broken, our trust lost
Any happiness will come at a cost.
We'll wait with worry for exam results
We'll be forced to hear all our faults.

We're not grown-up, that we can see
In fact, we're not sure we want to be
But we are not children like everyone says
We've kissed goodbye to our childhood days.

No, we're not big and we don't know it all
But sometimes you have to let us fall.
As long as you love us and will every day
We promise that we'll be OK.

So, mums and dads, this poem's for you
In case you want our point of view.

Hannah Thompson-Yates (14)

WHY ME?

Does it always have to be me
standing in a corner all on my own?
The loneliness inside me may terrify other children
if they saw it.

Does it always have to be me
being the bullied one?
The fear inside me
is enough to make the whole world cry.

When at home I sit in my room crying
Waiting for somebody to come
and comfort me.

Nobody at home, nobody at school,
In a way the world is empty.
Nobody at all, I cannot talk to anybody
If I do he'll get me
Somehow, some way.

Why does it have to be me
The one that always suffers constantly?
The one known as Billy No Mates.

If I tell somebody about him
I will end up suffering even more
He will kick me and punch me.

Walking home from school
Often leaves me in a state
'Behind you'
He shouts 'I'm going to get you'
A tear falls from my cheek once more.

No friends, no family that will
help me
Why does it have to be me?

Chris Barnard (14)

TEENAGER

I'm a teenager now
There are things I must do,
Like spend hours shopping
And waste money too.

I should ring up the phone bill,
Twelve pages long,
Spend years in the bathroom,
Paint make-up on.

I'm a teenager now
There are fights I should fight,
With my mother and father
To stay out all night.

With brothers and sisters
And fall out with friends,
To get my voice heard
In tears it all ends.

I'm a teenager now
There are decisions to make,
What grades I should target
And what subjects to take.

What boy to go out with,
What clothes should I wear?
What music to listen to,
What style in my hair?

I'm a teenager now,
But growing up fast,
I'm having great fun now,
How long will it last?

Claire Baker (14)

VAMPIRE'S LAIR

Ancient and isolated
The stone castle stands
Towering into the night sky
Terror of the lower lands.

A lonely traveller
Stumbles up the drive
Battered and weak
He's barely alive.

He makes it to the doorway,
Reaches for the handle,
But from the window, he doesn't see
A flick, the light of a candle.

Inside, dark and gloomy
Silence all around
Cobwebs in the corners
Huge rats on the ground.

He staggers up the stairway
To get to the higher floors,
He sees cracked stone arches,
Above old oak doors.

The wooden door creaks,
He opens it wide,
His warm blood freezes,
As wolves howl outside.

A dusty coffin lid opens
A cloaked figure grabs him
Bloodshot eyes, glistening fangs,
She has another victim.

Rachel Massey (13)

My Nicky Poem

Nicky is so gorgeous
I love him to bits
He is in my favourite band
And he's really fit.

Nicky has blue sparkling eyes
That once quickly glanced at me (I wish!)
He has a hunky six pack
And he's only twenty-three.

Nicky's the only person on who
I have a massive crush
At concerts I always scream for him
Because he is so lush.

He's really good at dancing
And he's really funny
He has charm, looks, charisma
And loads and loads of money.

Words to describe Nicky:
Gorgeous, lovely, fine,
Perfect, hunky, handsome
I wish he was all mine.

I've never ever met him
But I really hope I do
Sometime soon in my life
To make my dreams come true!

Laura Price (15)

One Day

One day I will
Be making a difference,
Be licensed to drive,
Be powerful,
Be the big cheese,
The high and mighty.
Be called, 'Ma'am.'
Be the person everyone wants in their circle of friends
Oh yes.
Be that woman in the hair commercial,
Be that voice flowing out of the stereo,
The face looking out from the cover of every magazine.
Those words jumping out from the book everyone needs.
Be 'In touch with mind, body and soul.'
Be happy
The kind of happy women's magazines yak about.
Strong, independent and most of all, bad-hair-day-retardant.
Be the interesting woman at the cocktail party.
Be a city hopper
London to New York and Las Vegas by Tuesday.
Be the person who politely refuses a beer and a ciggie.
Be Miss Jane Bond
Shaken, not stirred.
But right now, as I am,
Teenage and definitely not many of the above,
I am content to just
Be.

Meryl Trussler (13)

The Unspoken Language

The labyrinth
A maze of unique passages
Providing their individual clues.
Painting the portrait of their literal appearance,
On nothing but the plainest white sheet.

The mirage
An infinite vision
Found only by those seeking it -
Not dismissing it.
They accept the unreachable
As an object of faith.

The ocean
A continuous, immortal wave
The site for the unexpected to occur.
An outside appearance never to be judged
As the depth, at first, is never known.

The fruit
Produced by the flower
Containing the embryo of the future
Their taste will often vary
Though each survive for the same purpose.

Four clues,
Four wonders,
Four visions,
Four symbols,
Providing nothing more than the warmest joy
For any audience.
These are the four wonders of
The unspoken language -
A sound that communicates without speech.

Ruth Rimer (15)

FOOLISH

He twists, he turns
It blisters, it burns
It shot and surged
Right through him.

He flinches, he writhes
As it desperately tries
To find out
How to kill him.

He screams, he yells
His eyes turn red like the fires of Hell
He cannot tell
If it's killed him.

His tongue turns white
As he tries with his might
To stop and to fight
Its evil.

His mouth slips closed
They do not need to be told
That his evil foe
Has killed him.

If he had just thought before
He'd asked for one more
Of the things I deplore,
He'd still be here.

But temptation won
And favour of 'fun'
His life is now done
Cos it killed him.

Tom Preston (13)

Seasons Make Changes

In the summer
Days feel so long
That's because they are
The days just drag on
The hours seem to last forever
You get so hot and bothered
And flowers are in their full bloom.

In the autumn
The clock's hours fall back
So we get darker days
The days are colder
The hours feel normal
You wind down
And flowers begin to shrivel.

In the winter
Days are so short
Nights seem to come in the afternoon
The days aren't remembered
The hours fly by
You get so cold
And there are no flowers in sight.

In the spring
The clock's hours jump forward
Light becomes normal again
The days brighten
The hours seem new
Your energy is revived
And flowers begin to blossom.

Megan Preece (14)

I Dream Of . . .

I dream of being a tour rep,
Of being abroad and tanned for the whole holiday season,
Of going home in the winter,
Leaving the sunshine behind.

I dream of being a doctor,
Of helping and healing other people,
Of stabbing and slicing innocent flesh,
Controlling their life or death.

I dream of being a fashion designer,
Of being rich and famous and in all the magazines,
Of spending most of my time with stroppy stars,
Creating an infamous Oscar's gown.

I dream of being a ballerina,
Of dancing effortlessly around the stage with grace,
Of bleeding toes and aching feet,
Injured and unable to perform again.

I dream of being a soldier,
Of being surrounded by fit men all day,
Of being ordered around and constantly exhausted,
Risking my life for my country.

I dream of being a wife,
Of being someone else's world.
I dream of being a mother,
Of raising and watching my children grow up.
I dream of being a mother-in-law, sister-in-law, grandmother and aunty,
Of having family and friends I'm close to and love.

I dream of being happy.

Fiona Mackie (15)

School Life

'Wake up, wake up,'
Mum yells.
'Hurry up, hurry up,'
My sister screams.
Ring, ring
Goes the school bell.
'You're late, you're late,'
Says my form tutor.
Ring, ring
Goes the school bell.
Bang, bang
Go the doors as they slam shut.
'Chatter, chatter,'
Everyone's talking.
'Sit down, sit down,'
Says my RE teacher.
Ring, ring
Goes the school bell.
'Shut up, shut up,'
Yells all of my other teachers.
Ring, ring
Goes the school bell.
'Dinner time, dinner time,'
Our hungry stomach's shout.
Ring, ring
Goes the school bell.
Last lesson, last lesson
Hooray for home time.

Emily Bromfield (14)

Yesterday, Today, Tomorrow

Yesterday,
Yesterday I was young,
Oblivious to what was bad
Not getting what I wanted
Was all that made me sad.
Yesterday I was rosy-cheeked,
And everything was gay
All I ever seemed to do
Was sleep and eat and play.

Today,
Today I'm anti-government
I don't like those rules
I'd rather not be doing science,
On rock-hard, wooden stools!
Today everything's unfair
And nothing goes my way
Everything that needs to be forgotten
Always seems to stay.

Tomorrow,
Tomorrow I have fitted in
Into society
Problems finally gone away
Leaves peace for you and me.
Tomorrow nations all link hands
And sing a song of peace
Hopefully all of these good times,
Will never, ever cease.

Carl Pervin (13)

THE RUNNING RODENT RATS

Rats, rats, rats,
All around me
Long, cold, snaky tails
Cute, furry, soft rats.
Rats, rats, rats,
All around me
Dainty, ballerina toes
Giant rats, small rats.
Rats, rats, rats,
All around me
American rats, Scottish rats,
Snowy rats, muddy rats,
Sooty rats, sandy rats.
Rats run like hot air jets.
Rats, rats, rats,
All around me
Sharp-eyed, scurrying . . . rats!

Ashley Thomson (14)

MY FRIENDLY SURPRISE!

As I walked home from school one day
I had a look around
And there to my surprise I found
A cat upon the ground.
I picked it up and saw it had very little fur
I took it home and nursed it well,
And soon it began to purr!
It purred and purred then snuggled in with its head
Beneath my chin!

Ashley Bell (13)

SWEET SENSATIONS

The smell of roses caressing your hair
The colour washed over your sight.
Light summer's breezes stroking your skin,
The sun beating down; warm and bright.

Feeling your drink run down your throat
As you sip from your crystal clear glass
Hearing water splash in the paddling pool
And trickle down onto the grass.

Waking up early to hear the birds sing,
The morning light creeping through
Then falling back into your candy-filled dreams,
Before facing the day, fresh and new.

Tingling fingers, eyes wide and bright
Seeing the sun go down.
Watching the stars in the clear night sky
Wrapped up in your dressing gown.

Smelling the scent of your cosy bed,
And turning down the light.
Curled up like a baby, clutching your teddy,
Feeling warm and safe for the night.

Jumping in puddles in wellington boots,
Whether they're old or new.
And mountains of red, brown and golden leaves
Swept up and left just for you.

Opening your eyes on Christmas Day
Excitement sends your heart wild.
Fresh fallen snow glistening bright,
That reminds you of being a child.

Lying alone in your own little bubble,
Whenever, whatever the place.
Your bed, the grass, the silky sand
Living life at your own chosen pace.

Helen Kimber (15)

CHANGE IS . . .

Change is a dream
Lost and not found.
Change is a stream
All dried up on ground.

Change is when love turns
Into hate
Changes are future
What is your fate?

Change is peace
Pushed aside by war.
Change is great people
Being made poor.

Change is pure beauty
Turned into dirt.
Sometimes changes
Leave you hurt.

Whatever change is
It's not always bad.
Otherwise everyone on Earth
Would be sad.

Jessie Robinson (13)

Why Me?

Why me? I'm a good kid, I always abided by the rules,
But then it happened to me.
I wasn't doing anything,
I didn't even look at them
But no, prejudged by my height.
That was when it all changed,
That moment at the bus stop
Minding my own business and smack!
Why? I didn't even know them
They didn't even know me.
'You should be proud of yourself' they say,
'You never went down!'
So what if I never went down?
It shouldn't have happened in the first place
So then I did an ID parade
No one-way mirrors, just a room with twelve fellas,
Tall, dark-haired, slim, all looking the same,
Except for the lad who hit me,
I could recognise him a mile away
But the fear of facing him, two feet away,
Looking into his eyes.
Number six it was, easily spotted him,
And now there's a court case,
So they're all out to get me
His mates that is.
Lacerated face, a broken nose, totally unprovoked.
So now I'm looking around corners, absolutely paranoid
Staying indoors with my computer,
Watching the box constantly,
Ever-longingly wondering, what would have happened if . . .
. . . If I'd hit him back.
'You should have' people say
'You've a hard enough hit,
You could have floored him!'

Maybe so, but then I'd be up in that court.
He's pleading not guilty
But the evidence is all pointing the other way,
Witnesses telling otherwise,
Maybe I should have.
But it all goes back to that one question in the first place,
Why?

Luke Simpson

BALLAD OF A BUSH HEAD

My hair is wavy like the sea,
It's wild and thick and bounces free.
I would not have it another way,
But it is my torment every day.

It often seems to offend the eye,
Of everybody walking by.
While some shout comments right out loud,
Others give me looks that need no sound.

Everyone has to fit into society,
No one likes individuality
And because I don't fancy becoming a clone,
I am made a pariah and must stand alone.

Many have tried making my hair acceptable
I've been chased by straightners and all kinds of chemicals
But all have failed miserably that tried,
You just cannot control the tide.

I'm the prey of lower mortals, who never get bored,
And I'm fighting a constant battle against a sharp straightened sword.
But I will not be made afraid,
Because no one will ever tame my waves.

Hilary Carr (14)

A Pink Pig

I know a pink pig
Who wears a blond wig.
He likes white mugs,
And rolls in mud.
He sleeps all day,
And has piglets in May.
He likes to eat,
Especially meat.
He likes talking to girls,
All over the world.
He likes to snore,
Which can be quite a bore.
He has black spots,
That don't come off.
He has big ears,
And likes drinking beer.
He likes spending money
But turns his nose up at honey.
All day he trots around,
Trying to make no sound.

Emma Skillen (13)

Multicolours

As filters absorb the light to their soul
There becomes no colour left in the world
Excluded they are, rejected maybe
A stream of light is what glides them to see.

During the day as shadows pass by
They're no longer worthy, no tears left to cry
At night as the moon reflects in their hearts
Families on mind whom they had to depart.

As filters absorb the light to their soul
There becomes no colour left in the world
Excluded they are, rejected maybe
A glimmer of hope is enough left to see.

Matt Burrows (14)

THE WORLD WOULD BE A BETTER PLACE IF . . .

The world would be a better place if people were set free
Free to live their life the way it should be.
So tell me if you believe what I say is true
Would the world be a better place if stories like this were not true?
I am isolated, trapped and alone, not having a purpose for my life
But to please other people.
I feel like the greyness of the clouds coming over the sun
Not being able to bring happiness to people
Just because I wish to do what I want and choose.
I am my father's daughter and he only chooses my future.
I am forbidden to step beyond the gates of my father's place
And I must remain here until I marry my father's chosen groom.
No man is allowed to see a fleeting look of my flesh
For I wear a long black cloak
Hidden from the anxious eyes of my father's people.
It's not my fault I was born into this religion
But can't I choose what I believe in?
How I marry and where I go
Out of all the wonderful and precious gifts life can bring
Don't I deserve these three things.
I often think of women everywhere
Becoming things I never thought we could ever be
But will that day ever come for me?
Now tell me if you believe what I say is true
Would the world be a better place if stories like this were not true?

Yemisi Bokinni (13)

LONELINESS AND DEPRESSION

You're feeling hurt, you're feeling sad
You just want to cry when things go bad.
Inside of you you're crying so much
No happy feelings, no loving touch.

'Things will get better!' people say
But for you they get worse every day.
Lonely and depressed you're left alone
Trying to find your place at home.

Then you turn angry and are in denial
You see people laugh, jump and smile.
If they are so happy then why aren't you
Maybe it's something you forgot to do?

The pain you're feeling, rips you apart
But there is a place for you in someone's heart.
Look closely inside their eyes and find
The way to your happiness is in their mind!

You were so wrapped up in your depression and gloom,
That you blocked out everything else in the room.
But now you've opened up and given some time
So you can enjoy life like it is one big line.

Carly Gaskell (13)

KILLERS OF THE NIGHT

Twinkle stars,
Twinkle bright,
But dangerous are these twinkles out of sight.
Their fires are burning,
Their speed is ferocious,
So watch out for their size,
They are enormous.

Innocent they seem,
Innocent is their disguise,
But don't be fooled,
Because their beauty holds lies.
So sit back in knowledge,
But never go near,
Or one of these stars will make you disappear.

Gillian Vesco (15)

MONDAYS

You get out of bed still half asleep,
The next thing you hear is the bus go beep,
You clamber around as the bus drives away
Then you sit on the floor all full of dismay.

Your family's all left, you give up all hope,
You wash your face then drop the soap,
Everything's all wrong, you can't get to school,
That's the only part that's cool.

It's five to nine and still no luck
You think to yourself, doesn't life just suck.
Suddenly the phone rings and it's your dad,
Maybe this day isn't so bad.

Your dad comes home and drives you to school,
You can't find your class, you feel such a fool,
It's the first day back and you wish you were home,
You feel like your head's just an empty dome.

You sit in class next to your friend
Your new teacher drives you round the bend.
Well Monday comes and Monday goes
What happens next week, nobody knows.

Leanne Craig (13)

The Match Of The Season

. . . And there goes the whistle for the ninth month.
Summer comes out of the tunnel looking hot and sweaty,
While Autumn blows out a lot more lively.
The ref. drops the pumpkin and the game commences
Catherine Wheel to Fawkes, Fawkes passed to Witch
(Who is wicked)
Witch passes to Rocket and Rocket shoots high into the top corner
Summer's hopes are now looking dim and their defence is getting shaky.
Suddenly, Catherine Wheel spins down the line and crosses the pumpkin which deflects into the net!
There goes the whistle again to put Autumn ahead at half-time
The second half is less heated. It begins with a flurry when Leafie is brought down in the box.
He converts!
As time goes on Summer gives way to Autumn's strength,
Conceding again in the last minute.
Summer thinks it's all over. It is now!
Final score - Summer 0 - Autumn 3.

Nicholas Hughes (11)

National Park

The sun was shining through the many trees,
Following quickly was the gently breeze
The water trickled along a bubbling brook
While the tropical flowers were breathtaking with just one look.

The butterflies fluttered by and by
While the beautiful birds soared through the sky
The fish swam lazily through the water, so cool,
While insects crawled happily, alongside the pool.

The sun disappeared in its place was the moon,
The birds settled down, waiting to chirp their tune.
The forest was silent, calm and dark
As night had come again, in the national park.

Kirsty Oldfield (14)

THE WORLD AROUND US

You and I wake up every morning
Knowing that breakfast will be made,
Knowing that lunch will be cooked
And that dinner will be served.

Children in war-torn countries don't
They don't have a clue if a relative will be lost,
Or even if they will even see sundown tonight.
They have to scavenge for food,
While trying to keep alive in gun battles and minefields.

Poverty and anger are mixed with fear and emotions
In a war the cost of human life deteriorates,
Life is cheap for some, but not for the relatives of the dead.
Countries and lives destroyed by war,
Battle scarred landscapes and minefields.

Once the war is over and peace is declared,
The battle might be over for the soldiers,
But it carries on for the people in countries,
Unknown minefields and bombs endanger the lives of civilians for years to come.

You would have thought,
That humanity would learn after two world wars,
That war is the wrong answer,
Unfortunately
Humanity hasn't.

Carwyn Jones-Evans (15)

THE WORLD

The world is a home to every human, plant and animal
It is something that everyone has in common,
Whatever their sex, age or background.
So how come the world's in such a state?
People fighting, murdering and destroying the planet.
We all have to live here, there's no other place
And share it every day of our lives.
So why do we abuse it and the people in it?
It's the need for dominance in a world of equality.
The hunger for more land, authority and money.
I hope one day soon, others will realise this,
Put down their weapons and stop fighting,
Join together for a brighter future,
A future where generations to come will live in harmony,
In a world with no famine, war or abuse,
Where democracy and equality rules.
But most of all I hope,
Weapons will become like dinosaurs,
Extinct and a thing of the past.

Anneka Welstead (15)

THINK ABOUT IT

While you sit at your kitchen table
Young little Frederick is dying in a stable
While you're tucked up tight in bed
Don't forget to think about poor little Fred.
Just think about it.

People working in the mines
Carrying coal that breaks their spines,
People being whipped all day long
No windows open to rid of this pong.
Just think about it.

People dying every day
Then in their coffins they shall lay
Think how lucky we must be
To be able to buy food for our tea
Just think about it.

Christopher Lewis (14)

To My Dog Gypsy

To my dog Gypsy
Thanks a lot
You make me happy
And laugh a lot.

You're cute and cuddly
And funny too
Everything I ask of you
You will do.

You like to play
And run around
And when you find things
Shout 'Look what I've found!'

Your pretty face
Is full of expression
If anyone puts a foot wrong
You'll teach them a lesson.

So to my dog Gypsy
Thanks a lot
You make me happy
And laugh a lot.

Stefanie Harris (13)

LIFE'S ETERNAL REQUIEM

Crystal tears cascade down their cheeks
The winter's grasp so cold and bleak
As they lay a rose down on the ground . . .
Angels sing her requiem.

The sky joins in the mournful set
As raindrops fall, down the stone they crept
'Heaven holds her now,' they all say . . .
Begin her eternal sleep.

My thoughts are flooded with a thousand sorrows,
She'll see no more next weeks, no more tomorrows,
A life cut dead by nature's cruel wrath . . .
But who decides who's next?

Through her veil I see my mom battle tears
Her life now empty, an abyss of fears
Yet even she has come to accept . . .
Everyone takes a last breath.

So many things I wanted to tell her
How much I respected, admired and loved her,
But her journey took an unexpected turn . . .
Then again, doesn't everyone's?

My lasting tribute to a life so pure,
A tear? A flower? Grief so sure?
My words paint a dearer picture now . . .
Engraved in our memories always.

Her body lies where spirits roam
Now compelled to call Elysuim her home,
Her tomb is sealed with one last prayer . . .

'The shining sun will eventually set,
A newborn's life will fade,
Through seasons gone and seasons more,
And may you be remembered always!'

Alexandra Cook (15)

At The Movies

Movies are made to make
You laugh or cry,
Such as Scream, Ghost
And American Pie.

Scary, spooky, sadness
And death,
Movies are made to
Capture our breath.

Buckets of popcorn
What a treat,
Watching the movie
In your seat.

Choices are there
For everyone,
Cartoons comedy,
Action and lots of fun.

Go to the movies,
Don't delay
Book on-line the
Modern way.

Donna Moffatt (13)

MILLENNIUM DREAM

The traffic was horrendous, abysmal in fact
The cars bumper to bumper caused an enormous tailback
Walking to the stadium was a very long way
But the fans caused an atmosphere which added to the day.

Waiting for the players to emerge from underground
The cheering, singing, roaring, colourful sights, deafening sound
Onto the millennium pitch the players finally run
The excitement mounting, this day is going to be fun.

The first goal was scored in the Birmingham end
Robbie Fowler does it for Liverpool again and again
In injury time Birmingham equalised the score
My stomach is churning, I can't take any more.

My nerves were in shreds when the penalty shoot-out came
I really hope that Liverpool will score and win the game.
Carragher scored to make it five - four
Birmingham shoot, miss and the Liverpool fans gave a roar.

The Worthington Cup was presented to Liverpool team
Hope we will be back in May for another millennium dream.
I'm really glad I watched my terrific team play
The best manager in the world is Gerrard Houllier.

Ian Billington (13)

UNWANTED VISITOR

I came around the other day
Because my life was such a bore
No one was in, so I helped myself to the door.
I looked around the room
And my eyes were amazed to see

Everything laid out, especially for me.
I walked around the room
As quiet as a mouse.
I grabbed the things I wanted
And quickly left the house.

Sarah Cullen (15)

Too Late For You

You forever say you love me
But then you do these things you do
How can you explain my best friend
You thought I never knew.

Things won't ever be the same
Always creeping round behind my back
Thinking you were sly
Thinking you had the knack.

I loved you though all the rumours
I was there when you needed me
I can't believe it lasted so long
It was never right and it never will be.

So now I've had enough
For once I'm doing what's right.
You can find someone else to cheat on
I can't stand any more of these sleepless nights.

Always wondering where you were
And if you were coming home
I don't see you for days on end
Now you come home to an empty house
Alone.

Jacqueline Jacobs (13)

Poem About Teenage Life

Many adults like to say 'Teenage life, don't go there, no way!'
But what the adults seem to forget
Is that they were once one teenage pain in the necks.
Basically, teenage is all about fun,
The time before you turn into a grumpy pain in the bum.
Sure you may hate it, sure you may groan,
But just remember you're not alone.
Teenage life is mostly about, hanging out,
With your mates, your friends and usually a lout.
Kicking a footy, playing in the park
And getting up for school when it's normally dark.
School is a worry for many teens there,
Exams, maths and the headteacher's hair.
But for many at school, it's always a laugh, a doss,
And a sneaky chance to play on Super Mario Bros.
Adults keep saying that 'School is the best days of your life.'
I usually reply with a comment like 'Yeah right!'
Remember though, school is not just a drag,
It's the foundations of your life - just ask your dad.
And if there's one thing that high school's has ever taught me
It's that at the end of year eleven we shall all be free, yippee!

Andy Hughes (14)

I'm Tired

I'm tired of all the sadness in this world alone.
I'm tired of always losing my way and being far from home.
I'm tired of not being myself, trying to fit in.
I'm tired of the game Frustration, I never seem to win.

I'm tired of my sister nagging, thinking she's the boss.
I'm tired of Daddy shouting, whenever he gets cross.
I'm tired of having lots of homework, three or four each night.
I'm tired of being in darkness, hoping for some light.

I'm tired of having fruit salad, being forced to eat pear.
I'm tired of feeling lonely and thinking why life is unfair.
I'm tired of wearing school uniform, the colours navy and blue.
But most of all, above everything else, I'm tired of missing you!

Katy Johnston (13)

SPACE

Space, space, space
There's nothing in space
Held on by nothing
Not even a single lace.

He floats, boy does he float
He floats like a boat
On a shining, speckling moat.

His body is so still
Held on by nothing,
It gives him quite a chill.

Miles above the Earth, he is
His wife and children
He'd like to kiss.

Gliding across the moon
Is he walking to his doom?

To his ship he returns
His fellow spacemen take it in turns
To walk the walk of the moon
Are they also walking to their doom?

They have now completed their mission
They now go back to Earth
Back to their civilisation.

Glenn Wall (13)

Undertaker's Heart

He lurks round the corners
Waiting for me to turn
His eyes are full of fire
That blazes his soul.

Love is a feeling, love is pure
With a heart like his, there is no cure.
He hurts who he touches, his love is unpure
Undertaker, undertaker, undertaker's heart.

He haunts my dreams,
He haunts my life,
Even now he's gone, his icy mark still freezes my blood
He feeds on other's pain, to feed his greedy heart
Undertaker, undertaker, undertaker's heart.

Now there's someone new and love is once again pure
But his burning eyes still singe my mind
For he is evil, he is cold but he has an . . .
Undertaker, undertaker, undertaker's heart.

Kerri Dickens (14)

Heavy Metal Music

Heavy metal music playing all the time,
Heavy metal music a brilliant friend of mine,
Heavy metal music playing all the time,
It can blow your speakers and even blow your mind.

Heavy metal music rocking all day long,
Heavy metal music surely nothing's wrong,
Your parents can't stand it and turn the music off
So you run upstairs and play it in the loft.

Heavy metal music pounding in your ears,
Heavy metal music will chase away your fears,
Heavy metal music will bring you peace of mind,
Heavy metal music, a brilliant friend of mine.

Richard Reid (13)

DREAMCATCHER

Your thoughts, your visions, your dreams
Are what are in the clouds
Projections of figures in the sky
Ribbons of ideas weave the roots of the dream
The end is the limit of your imagination
I see no finish line in sight.

Your dreams are the guests
That interact with you in your mind
They feel as real as the rays blaze your skin
And the breath of the breeze stroking your cheek
But when the day shifts to night
The odd unwelcome arrives.

Yet a dreamcatcher is the net draped with ribbons
And dressed with rosewood beads
To detected the uninvited ones
To fish out the ill thoughts
A guardian, a protector and a defender
To shield out bad dreams.

So when the sun slumps down into the valleys
And the night chariot rules the sky
In darkness they think you're vulnerable in their sight
The dreamcatcher knight arise
To banish then distant and far away
To open the door for sweet dreams.

Tina Lau (14)

The Moon

The moon, why is it here?
Where does it come from?
Why do we only see a little bit?
Is it there just to look pretty?

The moon could be there for a reason
But I think it brightens up the cloudy, dark sky
But sometimes we even see it in the daytime, why is this?

Who put the moon there?
But does it travel around the world or what?
There are so many questions I want to ask
But I only have a short number of lines to do it.

Why is there only one moon there?
Why can't there be two or three?
What is the meaning of the moon, stars and the sun?
Why does the moon only come out at night?

Oh well, these questions are not going to get answered
But why is the world here?
What's the meaning of us?
Why do we only live once and then die?

Does the moon have a face?
Why does the moon change shapes each night?
Is it a regular thing or does it happen once in a while?
How many faces does the moon have?

Gemma Atkins (13)

My Best Friend

She's funny and sweet,
She's got smelly feet,
With brown hair
And a mean glare,
With one stare you're out of there.

She's fun and cool,
Especially at school,
Her eyes are blue,
You stick to her like glue,
Cos she's my best friend.

Julie Reynolds (13)

CHANGING VIEWS

A reflection matters,
If only
The mirror lied
Or broke in my hands
Appearances matter
And words cut deep
Girls' words make a difference
Fill my diary
Take away my self-confidence
Attempts to be accepted
Fail -
And drag me down.

Caught up in my emotions
My dreams are ever changing
(Often erased)
Temperament and aspirations vary -
I am no child
So misunderstood
Rejected by adults
And stereotyped.
My head stands tall,
Above the sweet counter
The lemon fills my mouth with bitterness
A different view.

Camilla Gare (15)

A LEGEND NAMED JOHN

Sometimes when I'm feeling down there's a thought that sees me through
A thought of this man and his band singing 'Love Me Do'
I think the four are legends, I have them on my wall,
I always wish that I could meet, John, George, Ringo and Paul
But when they went their separate ways one man still marched on,
That man married Yoko, that man's name was John.
He said he wanted peace and love, his music says the same,
His music is still remembered, his music had brought him fame.
All his songs express his views, the words all mean a lot,
But one sad night his life was taken and the legend was shot.
Sometimes when I think of John I look up to the sky
'Imagine there's no Heaven, it's easy if you try'.
So if there is a Heaven and we go there when we die,
I know John will be there, watching from a high
Although dead for twenty-two years his memory still lives on,
We still think he is a legend, we still remember John.
And through his music I feel he's alive, even though he has gone,
Thank God for John Lennon, the legend still lives on.

Peter Moseley (15)

TEENS

Teens are mental,
Teens are mad,
Teens are mixed-up
But I'm not.

Teens are tall,
Teens are small,
Teens are medium
But I'm perfect.

Teens are smelly,
Teens are gross,
Teens are muddy,
But I'm clean.

Dads don't understand us,
Mums don't understand us,
Sisters don't understand us,
But I do.

Kane Moore (13)

Hacker

Fingers slowly drifting across the keyboard,
Which key to press? What word to say?
So confusing, yet so obvious,
Why do I do this?
What's my reason for doing this?
I should switch off now,
But I can't, can I?

The word is on the tip of my tongue, it's just not there,
I know everything, yet I know nothing
I am isolated, yet I am in there with all the gossip
Do I even have a life worth living?
I need someone to tell me,
But there is no someone,
I don't know anyone.

I can reach out to those who I know,
And to who I don't know,
The ones I've never met or dreamed of meeting,
They don't know who I am, do I know who I am?

Aly Rickard (13)

The Crocodile

Gliding in the water,
Moving like a snake,
Twisting round and round,
What move will he make?

Grinding his sharp teeth,
Stretching his strong tail,
If he reaches his prey,
He surely will not fail.

Suddenly he moves,
Swimming at fast speeds,
Destroying his cover,
Charging through the reeds.

Swinging his tail quickly,
Snapping his jaws,
Going as fast as possible
As he roars.

Swish, snap,
Plod, roar,
The prey won't worry
Any more.

Christopher Martin (13)

Horses And Ponies

Horses and ponies are really fun
Trotting, galloping up and down
Putting on babies for piggy back rides
On their faces are never a frown.
Putting on tack and raring to go
On a hot and sunny day

Going on a pleasant beach ride
Where they think they can get their own way.
Shoulder in a figure of eight
Is all in the event of dressage
And after a hot and humid day
They get a lovely back massage.

Mary Prescott (13)

Parents

The word says it all . . . Pa-rents
As soon as you are born the rent starts
From your very first word - 'Mummy'
Then changing to - 'Money'
Parents always saying 'No more money.'
But us in our teens say 'Just a little bit more'
Otherwise it's slamming of doors
And 'I hate you with tears and more.'
Then the father says,
'Don't cry any more,
Have some pounds to spend on your trends.'
Happy as a sand boy
You take the money and rush out the door
Then all you're left with is
Your brother saying, 'Please Mum
Please Dad, can I have some more?'
So you return from having your day of fun
To find that your mum and dad are saying,
'You got your money
Tidy your room or . . .
You won't get any more!'

Parents!
We love you really.

Cara Rawlinson (14)

TERROR

The world is reined by terror
But when I look in the mirror
It's a peaceful place
No discrimination against our race.

But when I look away
The world turns to dismay.

World leaders try, but don't endeavour
Destroying innocent lives forever
Doing so the situation escalates
Meaning a lot higher death rates.

The world puts out a cry of plea
Just to stop such insanity
Some of these world leaders are hypocrites
Want peace but will not call it quits.

Peace should be, war should be a binning
But for most of them it's just about winning
This is a feud, which will never get solved
But for me, I'll never get involved.

Micheal McKenna (14)

TIME

Time . . .
Is everywhere,
It's everything,
Nothing can tame it,
Nothing can stop it,
Everything is ruled by it,
But nothing can see it.

Time is . . .
An endless circle,
Forever moving,
Never stopping,
Always forward . . .
Never back.
Time . . .

Jennifer Ames (13)

MR PERKINS SANG TO MISS TOKEN

'Come live with me and be my love
To you I will prove,
That I love in your sleep
My love for you is very deep.

And will sit upon cloud nine
With rays from the sun our faces shine,
Flowers spring up in sheer delight,
If only this was at night.

I will buy you ten red roses,
The smell will tickle both our noses,
We'll sit in the garden and bask in the sun
But when it gets dark we will eat, yum.

You will have the brightest dress,
No ladies can compare with your finesse,
Your shape is like a ten pin bowl
But I don't expect you're very old.

If you say no,
I will be heartbroken
So please marry me
Miss Token.'

Mary Hollyman (13)

The Creatures Of Myth

The creatures of myth make their arrival
Each one fighting, fighting for survival
The dragons breathe fire, the heat is immense
Their roars make the silent atmosphere tense.
The banshees are screaming, their language unknown
While the stare of Medusa turns her enemies to stone
Only the angels hide from the fight
Staying out of other creature's sight.
But one by one they're dragged into battle
And killed like wolves, chasing the cattle.
Soon the Devil arrives on horses of four
He has a taste for blood and is wanting more.
Then through the ground, the battle fell
Into the fiery depths of Hades' Hell
Then the creatures of myth through the fire and fog
Come face to face with Hades' three-headed dog
The barks of Cerberus shake the ceiling
And strip the creatures of any feeling
In the depths of Hell is where they'll always be
Fighting for all eternity.

Jonathan Claxton (15)

The Rose

Smell its beauty with your nose,
The wonderful fragrance of the rose.

The spiky thorns on its stem
Prick your fingers, pain again!

It's big and bold, bright and red
But tomorrow morning it might be dead.

Its petals fall day by day,
We know it will end this way.

Don't waste your tears when it has died,
As something new will grow deep inside.

Meg Rayner (13)

I Had A Dream

I had a dream
You were there
We were on a distant planet
Away from trouble, away from disaster
Then you went
I was alone
Everywhere was silent
I felt different
I don't like being alone
I need someone to share my feelings
So you came back
And you said,
'I'm a true friend.'
Friends should be there for each other
So you stayed, we shared secrets
I trusted you
The world needs a friend like you
No racist remarks
Do you know who you were?
You were a different culture and colour
But it didn't matter
I had a friend
I wasn't alone any more
I wish this wasn't a dream
I hope it's the future.

Emma Tomkinson (14)

LIFE LEARNING

I've learned selflessness
Although I know keeping myself
Happy is important too
And by helping others find
Happiness creates self happiness.

I've learned to take a step back,
To look at the big picture,
Before opening my mouth in complaint.

I've learned self-confidence
But I must keep reminding myself
That this trait should be used carefully
Appearing over-confident often hides truth.

Over everything, I've learned
That I still have much to learn
And everything I learn will not come out of books.
That the most valuable lesson
Comes from living.

Robyn Evans (15)

WHO IS MY ENEMY? WHO IS MY FRIEND?

Who is my enemy?
Who is my friend?
The one who ignores,
The one who pretends,
The one who watches,
As I suffer in pain

The one who shelters,
Me from the rain.
The one who smiles as I walk by,
The one who waves when I say hi.
Who is my enemy?
Who is my friend?

Stevie Hopwood (14)

UPSIDE DOWN

The world is such a funny place
So many odd things happen
It often makes me feel like spaghetti
You know, all tangled up - and messy.

Being a teenager,
It ain't half hard
People just don't understand
Anxiety, loneliness and confusion
These feelings are ever so awful
Upside down, round and round
God, when will it all end?

Greasy hair, spots
Homework and enemies
So hard to cope, on top of everything else
And I often feel so alone
But what can we do?

People say the teenage years
Are meant to be the happiest time of your life
Well where did that ever come from?
Adults need to relive this time
Then maybe they would realise!

Amy Coombs (13)

GIRLS AND BOYS

Boys.
Boys can be mad,
Boys can be sad,
But all the girls love 'em.
Boys think they're the best
Don't care about the rest
But all the girls still love 'em.
Boys can be rude,
Boys can be cheeky,
But girls still love 'em whoever they are!

Girls.
Girls are pretty,
Girls are witty
And the boys just love 'em.
Girls like to flirt
But hate the dirt
And boys still love 'em.
Some girls dress in pink
Others just wink
And boys just really love 'em.

Abigail Furley (13)

LOVE, HATE AND ENVY

A budding rose reminds us of love,
Each person will love in their life.
God loves in the shape of a dove,
As each man searches for a wife.

Hate has came to the world and risen,
Hate could lead to a fight.
Hate could sometimes lead to prison,
People know that hate isn't right.

Envy is a powerful emotion,
People envy, so do you.
Envy is an extremely bad notion,
Feel sorry for the people it happens to.

In all I think emotions are great,
But envy is the worst.
I hope I will never hate
And love could sometimes hurt.

Stephanie Batt (13)

Lessons

Maths, maths, what a bore
Ian's asleep and starts to snore.
Stabbing pencils into arms
Half the kids belong on farms.

Drama, drama, so much fun
Janet wants to be the nun.
Performance time has come - oh no!
Come on everyone, let's just go!

French, French, is the worst,
I need the toilet, I'm gonna burst!
But I should have gone at lunch or break
I'd better make it, for the teacher's sake!

History, history, what to say
It's so bad in every way.
Who was that and when was this?
Do you actually know the answer Miss?

Tech, tech, is the best
At least it's better than all the rest.
Hammering and sawing this and that
What am I making? It looks like tat!

Kate Rolfe (13)

The Orange That Had No Taste

Once I had an orange,
But the orange had no taste,
So I ate it in huge chunks,
To dispose of it with haste.

It was a seedless celmentine,
Easy peel it said on the bag,
Everything described was true,
But to eat it was such a drag.

So this little orange,
In my stomach as it sits,
But in segments, it is no longer,
For now it rests in bits.

It gave me but a little pleasure,
When its skin came off in a coil
But for what point did I unwrap it?
Oh how I wasted that toil.

So this little orange,
Like its friends and family yet to come
Won't be remembered for much longer,
But for the moment it fills my tum.

Rebecca Gent (13)

Being A Teenager

Being a teenager's fine
But not if you have a family like mine.
My brothers trash my make-up
And angry I do take up.
My sisters nick my tops
And listen to my pop.

My mum won't get me a phone
And wonders why I moan.
My dad won't take me shopping
Until I do some mopping.
Being a teenager's fine
But not if you have a family like mine.

Jessica Hupé (13)

MY FAMILY

I love my family
I really do
But something strange,
Makes me stew.

Is it their habit?
Or telling me off
Or something else
I'm not sure what.

Is it the homework?
They make me do
Or something other
That makes me stew?

Maybe the skirt
They make me wear,
Or something weird,
I just can't bear.

I'm not sure what
It really is,
But what I know
I love them to bits!

Jessica Henson (13)

May God Be With You All

(In remembrance of all who were killed in the September 11th terrorist attacks.)

What started out a normal day,
Quite soon turned out to be
One of the most horrific days,
Our nation's ever seen.

The world came to a standstill
Innocent lives snatched away,
Whilst the rest of us watched in disbelief
Not knowing what to say.

Our prayers and thoughts are with you all
The nations at your side,
They may have ripped out New York's heart,
But don't let them take your pride.

To those who lost their loved ones,
May God be with you all,
May He give you hope in times of doubt
And strength each time you fall.

To think of what you're going through
The heartache and distress,
We send our love to all of you
America, God Bless.

Laura Brown (14)

War

I don't know how you can cope
The pain,
The noise
And what you saw,
The bombs,

The bodies,
The smells,
The cuts and bruises,
The families that you missed
And the torture you went through.

Florence Aylieff-Sansom (14)

Inside My Head

Inside my head I'm in charge
Nobody else knows what's going on in there
The only person allowed in is me
I'm the only one who can see.

Inside my head I'm my own boss
Nobody can tell me what I should think
The only person allowed in is me
I'm the only one who can see.

Inside my head there's a different world
Nobody can see the thoughts spinning around
The only person allowed in is me
I'm the only one who can see.

It's the place where I'm in control,
The place where I go to hide.
Here I have space to stop and breathe
In myself I confide.

Inside my head there's loneliness
Nobody else can take it away.
The only person allowed in is me
I'm the only one who can see.

Sarah Evans-Wrench (13)

My Granny

My granny, she can barely talk
She can't get up or go for a walk
She told me all about her life
She only once threatened grandpa with a knife!
When she was young she fell in love
She said it was like being hit from above
His name was Jimmy and they got married
Had three children, Beth, Ben and Harry.
She told the nurses she was independent
She could look after herself and not be a defendant.
They wouldn't turn the machine off
She wanted to die, not have them panic over a cough.
They talked to her like a child
And she is very mild.
They say she could go any day
She said to let her die on her say.
When she spent that week with us
She made us happy, as she talked and fussed.
She told us she was once a bus driver,
She also said she was an expert driver.
Every second with her was not a minute to waste
As she lies on her bed with her big empty case
Then all of a sudden the machine stopped
From living to death, she was gone.

Leanne Hearn (14)

Summer

The birds singing in the trees,
Children playing in the street
People going to the beach,
People eating ice creams.

Out comes the sun lotion - factor thirty
Light, airy evenings
Evening drives in the country
Barbecue smells floating in the air.

Stephanie Oliver (13)

FRIENDS FOREVER

Going out to parties
Dancing about free
Friends forever
Just you and me.

Hold you when you're sad
Comfort you when you cry
Give you advice
About your guy.

Tell each other everything
Secrets unleashed
Things you don't know
Your best mate teaches.

Friends forever
You taught me how to be me
And fly, friends forever
Till we both die.

Then in Heaven
If you die before me
Wait and we can be together
Forever and free.

Tina Winton (15)

TEEN CRUSH

My first teen crush
Was totally lush.

I thought I was the best
He looked away and said, 'Who's next?'

He is in my dreams
He always answers to my screams.

He is always good with his feet
And he never seems to cheat.

I've wondered if he was good at school
But if I asked him I'd feel a fool.

He's the best boy I know
I really think so!

He's smart, he's young and always wants to win
And every time I see him he has a handsome grin!

His talent is always growing
My first crush is Michael Owen!

Lisa Adams (14)

YOUR ROOM

Your room
A place to hide when full of gloom
To cry those tears
Of secret fears
When all the world seems to be against you
And you don't know what to do.

All you need is someone to chase away your fears,
And wipe away the tears,
To set you on your way again
Like sunshine after the rain
Ready to face anything!

Rachel Bulman (15)

What Makes A Friend?

A friend is someone who doesn't care
What you look like or what you wear.
They don't mind what you do
Because they're always there for you.

When you're in doubt
A good friend is always about.
Friends are always ready to listen,
But when they're gone you really miss them.

A friend is someone with whom you have a laugh
And they don't care when you act daft.
You always have fun around them
And no one can ever be compared to them.

Friends never let you down,
Because they are always around.
They know you inside out
And know when and why you are doubt.

What makes a friend?
Someone who is always there
And will never let you down
That is what makes a friend.

Rianna Hooke (13)

DRIFTING INTO SPACE

The sky is black with twinkling stars,
I'm so alone,
No one near,
No one far.
I'm drifting into space,
With nobody in sight
I see blue planets
Yellow, red and white.
I'm nearly at my death,
I guess this is goodbye,
I don't know what I feel,
I can't laugh, scream or cry.
Goodbye.

Mary Morgan

ONE SMALL STEP FOR MAN

It is one small step for man
Walking on the moon,
Sending a satellite to Mars,
Finding new comets,
Taking pictures of planets.

But what about our planet?
The vicious wars fought?
The destruction of the forests?
When we learn to care about this,
It would truly be,
One giant leap for mankind.

Jennifer Atkins (15)

Feelings

The slight of emotion
The depths of your ocean
The spires of heat
You filled with your heart
And the hours of devotion
Showing so bland
The shocking cold surface
I could never understand
And the dent in it all believed by your call
The fine understanding
So brittle and broke,
And the warm, hard centre
That now makes me choke.
So don your ignorance
For secluded eyes dance,
The refreshing sensation
Of the puzzle now solved
Was the fly on the wall
In everything and all.

Clare Walsh (13)

Sadness

S adness is grey
A nd it tastes like the salty sea
D own in the dumps
N obody likes feeling sad
E veryone likes to be happy.
S adness is a summer's day with no sunshine.
S adness is leaving your childhood behind.

Carly Edwards (13)

BEAUTY

Beauty is something that cannot be defined,
Not by perfection and dressing up to the nines.
The right look, fashion and style alone won't attract
The people you want -
Trust me, it's a fact!

You can buy the in jewellery to look your absolute best,
To match the v-neck top that shows half your chest,
But will it go with those shoes you bought?
It was all colour co-ordinated -
So you'd thought.

If you're not totally perfect,
It doesn't really matter.
Your make-up may not be exact,
But personality is what will flatter.

Being on the large side may be getting you down,
But the smile you have is far better than any pretty girl's frown.
The personality stored inside your being
Will affect the person that all others are seeing.

It's easy to look pretty in pink or gorgeous in gold,
Beautiful in blue and to do as you're told.
But the real macoy of beauty isn't found in a store,
And if you look really deep inside yourself . . .
You'll find an infinite supply of more.

Carla Rankin (15)

BEST FRIENDS

When you need that shoulder to cry on
Your best friend is always there
To tell your secrets and problems
When you really need their care

To be there for each other
Side by side,
Hand in hand,
A friend like that is a friend for life.

Debbie Alcorn (14)

A School Day Dream

I go to school at half-past eight
And meet my friends at the gate
We go to form and chat for a bit
Until Miss comes and tells us to sit.

We go to our first class
Hurry up! Please and pass
Morning drags, please come to an end
The teachers are driving us round the bend.

Lunch is here, some time on our own
I bet the teachers are having a moan
We chat some more with our friends
We're not very happy when it ends.

Only two lessons left today
They come to an end; hope Miss doesn't make us stay
School has ended that is great
I'll meet my friends back at the gate.

On the bus and home we go
All that homework; oh no
We get ready and go out to play
We have the most fun we've had all day.

Today has ended; what a shame
Hope tomorrow's not the same.

Rachael Fraser (14)

THOSE TERRIBLE TEENAGE YEARS

Through the troubled times of a teenager's jumbled existence,
Life seems baffling and a mystery to most.
Some are flamboyant and excel at all things,
Others are humble and prefer not to boast.

School is a must but for many it's frustrating,
'What's the point?' they all cry. 'We'd rather not go.'
With rules and regulations, homework and tests,
All that it serves to do is inflict deep feelings of woe.

Outside this confinement young people feel free,
There are cinemas and shopping centres all for the taking.
Such a contrast to the days our grandparents were young
When boys would work hard while the girls mastered baking!

We're told to be grateful for the things we now have,
And give thanks every night for these 'gifts from above'
But all that is needed to keep us at ease,
Is a little bit of tenderness and compassion and love!

Nicola Whitehead (15)

MY SPECIAL MEMORY

My dad is the best, the best in the world
He is soft, cuddly and kind
He is six feet six or so he says
I know he's lying but I don't mind
And he will always be mine.

My dad is the best, the best in the world
He always treats me right
And we hardly ever fight
When we do he's kind of scary
But I love him the same
And he'll always be mine.

My dad is the best, the best in he world
The only problem is he doesn't exist
He died when I was seven
And all that's left is this
That's in my memory.

Olivia Mansworth (13)

AN IMAGE OF DEVON

A patchwork quilt of fields
Stretches across the horizon
Each part fitting together like a green jigsaw
Every segment enclosed by a hedge or fence
Keeping the animals in
And trespassers out.

A vulture of the ocean
Wheels in the sky
Atmosphere blending with sea,
Like different shades in a watercolour painting
Waves gallop as the wind
Foam and cloud become one.

A clash of metal
Echoes purely through the air
Vibrating through the cliffs
And combining with whale songs below
A flag is held aloft,
As Britain is reminded of her history, for a brief while.

The thunder of hooves
Sound like drums of war
As a medieval tournament unfolds,
Banners flutter aloft, ladies give tokens
And knights relive the glory
That once graced this isle.

Kirsty Little (15)

FIRST DATE

Her nails are painted a shade that would put fuschias to shame
She glances at him
But he's deep inside his brain
If only she had something to say
Instead she looks at her nail paint
Whilst deciding if the silence is romance
Or just a case of major tongue ache.
She would like to ask 'Is that really chocolate in your eyes?'
Instead she counts the splashes of rain
And endures the torment of first date.
As they sit here in the midst of nothing to say
The bench they are sitting on sympathetically cuts the silence with a remark
'Shitty weather, eh?'

Anna Magdalino (15)

FRIENDSHIP

Friendship is like a cosy sofa always there for you.
Friendship is like harmony in the ocean.
Friendship is like a torch lit in the darkness.
Friendship is like all flowers blossoming in summer.
Friendship is like dolphins swimming together.
Friendship is like the twinkling of stars at night.
Friendship is like dancing in the meadows.
Friendship is like a rainbow after the rain.
Friendship is like the sparkling of diamonds.
Friendship is like a colourful new world.
Friendship is like the sun setting on a hot summer's day.
Friendship is like music flowing in the valleys of paradise.
Friendship is like an exciting adventure.

Aliya Haider (13)

The Box

I locked it away in a box,
Because everything it contained was everything I hated and loved.
The things that made me angry beyond the depths of Hell,
But as happy as paradise
It held blinding light and pitch-black darkness in its confusion
Always, it brought me pain and agony,
But helping me and healing me every day.
So strong yet so weak,
So simple yet so complicated,
Scared, confused and eternally lonely,
But brave and preserving.
When I opened the box it overtook me and everything about me,
When I opened the box I saw myself.

Francesca D'Souza (15)

Three Best Friends

Everyone says two is company
And three is a crowd
Correct
Seats on buses
Fairground rides,
Everything's done in twos
Me sat all alone
They had left me
Three best friends no more.
Now though I have
Four best friends
Which is much better than two
Don't you think?

Louise Featherstone (15)

The Depths Of Revenge

Darkness lives 24/7
Never to enter Heaven
Hell is the birthplace
If it's set free it will end the human race.
Darkness is like a dark fog
Like a heart which is soon going to clog
Say goodbye to your soul
The will be turned black as coal.
You will be owned by Satan forever
Your freedom will never return, never!
Carnage will survive
It will be kept in your mind like archives.
If it sticks its teeth into your body
You remember nobody.
It's hungry for blood
It will wash you away like a flood
The fire will burn
And soon you will turn
Sanctuary has gone
Everything has gone wrong.

Matthew Stannard (14)

Tree

His life began as a seed,
Planted in the ground,
One summer's day the seed was found
And the rain and sun came down.
All the birds looked as they flew by
The tree grew and grew
To reach the sky.

Cheryl Fuller (15)

Christmas

Christmas, Christmas a happy time of year
Getting presents fills us up with cheer.
Pretty decorations all round the room,
Listen to the music of the Christmas tune,
Then watching television, a programme to be seen,
At three o'clock on Christmas Day a message from the Queen.
We are feeling contented with an inner glow,
Whilst outside it's freezing and the sky is full of snow.
We've opened all our presents, there's no more to be done,
They've kept us all amused, we sure have had some fun.
We've eaten lots and lots, we can't eat any more,
Tomorrow morning, our tummies will be sore.
Now we're feeling tired, it's time to go to bed,
We're looking for a place, to rest our weary head.
There is no doubt that all of us have had a lovely day,
All we've done all the time is eat, sleep and play.

Lisa Buttery

Hospital

Quickly I ran,
Quickly the bus knocked me,
Quickly the people crowded,
Quickly the ambulance came,
Quickly I was in hospital,
Quickly the nurse called the doctor,
Quickly he came,
Quickly I was in theatre,
Quickly they operated,
Quickly Mum and Dad came,
Slowly I passed away.

Kate Reid (13)

WHO AM I?

I am the friend that warms your heart
My cheerful colour makes you feel no longer alone.
I am the companion that can warm every part,
When the winter winds moan.
I am the enemy to any shiver,
My bright colours remind you of a Christmas tree,
My flames of love flow like a river,
But remember never play with me.
Pretty possessions sit on my shelf,
Surrounding of wood and stone,
Displaying all of your worldly wealth,
Without me you would feel alone.
Cards sit on my mantle with festive rhyme,
This will give you a clue perhaps in time.

Nicholas Allum (14)

PRISONER OF MY MIND

The birds sing a happy tune
But I feel locked in a cage held prisoner by my own mind.

They peck at my soul, the squawking and flapping will never cease
I am locked in a cage held prisoner by my own mind.

The birds beckon the weak of mind eating their heart
But not me for I am locked in a cage held prisoner by my own mind.

My heart is black, broken by past experiences
These are my thoughts, my feelings, my life,
For I am locked in a cage held prisoner by my own mind.

Sean Russell (14)

What It's Like Being A Teenager

Being a teenager is hard,
You never know what's on the card,
With loads of grades and exams,
Even having nagging mams.
Stress levels are on a high
Even if there's a gorgeous guy,
Friends know best
So make sure you have a rest.
You might want to reach for a tissue,
As money becomes an issue,
Having none at all, I mean
Get a job, you should be keen.
A job with good pay,
That won't last all day.
Homework has to be done as well,
Make sure it's before the bell.

Charlotte Ellis (14)

The Dream Seller

The dream seller walks amongst us
Blowing dreams into our minds like children blow bubbles.
Dreams that are often scorned, laughed at,
Driven from our midst
But sometimes the dream takes root
Is watered, sprouts and grows.
Think how much we can achieve
When the dream seller helps us to believe,
When he is on our side
An eternal optimist.
The dream seller walks amongst us.

Ciar McAndrew (13)

TEACHERS

Teacher, who or what are teachers?

Some teachers are nice,
Some speak as quietly as mice,
Some are strict,
And some are great fun and even play tricks.

Some teachers are kind,
Some even don't mind,
Pay attention or they might give you detention,
If you are late but not too often.

Teachers in general are good at what they do
And without them we would all be at a loss,
But they do like to be boss.
Teachers, yes teachers.

Alexandra Matthewson (14)

LIKE WATER FOR CHOCOLATE

Like the ocean, I ride your waves
And you make me scream in octaves.
Like a stream, you gently move me,
Sending shocking ripples right through me.
Like an oasis, you're much longed for,
You quench my thirst and so much more,
I'll ride your river till I reach the land
In hope of a reward by your hand,
Come splash on the rocks on the edge of my sea,
Then like water for chocolate,
Melt for me.

Rola Aina (15)

Under Attack

A year ago on September 11th disaster struck America,
Terrorist attacks on The Pentagon and World Trade Center.
Thousands of innocent lives suddenly ended,
Our loved ones have survived,
The people pretended.

The searching began very soon after,
As the truth sank in about the painful disaster.
Grief, tears and complete devastation,
Spread throughout the world and the nation.

A spared moment to pay our respects,
Three minutes silence to stop and reflect.
Sympathy and condolences to the grieving families.
Forever they will stay in loving memory.

Our sincere thanks to those who searched 24/7.
Justice will be done,
And the world will finally live as one.
God bless the angels who ascended to Heaven.
R.I.P.

Amelia Harrison (15)

My Day At The Races

My day at the races was fun
Watching all the horses run.
It was lovely and sunny
As we won lots of money.
It was good, it didn't rain
And I'd love to go again.

Francesca Newman (13)

Eternal Struggle

I'm not myself anymore,
I haven't been for about two years.
A spectator of the girl in the mirror,
Who has wept so many tears.

Homework has crushed her social,
Textbooks shackle her down.
She sits at her desk not understanding,
Longing to be out on the town.

Eruptions of evil punctuate her skin,
They glare at the world angrily.
Lotions and potions can't make them budge
Why can't they just leave her be?

Tears have stained her ashen face,
Yet an hour ago it was all grins.
Be careful to tiptoe round this one,
Or release the banshee within.

Inside a painful yearning,
Courses through her very being.
A passion for all things boy-shaped,
Like a pendulum are her feelings.

The girl in the mirror stares blankly,
As if she just can't see,
Who is the woman she has become?
Look closer, squint, it's me!

Amanda Shaw (15)

TEACHER, TEACH ME

Why is the sky blue not green
And why do the stars shine and gleam?
Why do the planets orbit the sun
And why is Jupiter the bigger one?
I ask you why?

Why do scientists experiment on rats
And why do cows eat the grass?
Why in war is there pain
When it keeps happening again and again?
I ask you why?

Why do we work and play
While my pet hamster sleeps all day?
Why do boys hang about
While all the girls scream and shout?
I ask you why?

Why is France an hour in front
And are they so different than us?
Why is the grass always green
And trees so tall and easily seen?
I ask you why?

Why are girls hot and sexy
And the boys cool and handsome?
Why am I writing this
For you all to sit and stare at it?
Why?

Thomas Locker

Best Friends

Best friends always
Remember so well
All the things they did together,
All the subjects they discussed,
All the mistakes they made,
All the fun they had.

Best friends always
Remember how their friendship
Was such a stabilising force
During confusing times
In their lives.

Best friends may have
Different lifestyles
Live in different places
And interact with different people
But no matter how much
Their lives may change
Their friendship remains the same.

I know that throughout my life
Wherever I am
I will always
Remember so well
And cherish our friendship
As one of the best
I have ever known.

Kavitha Suhumar (14)

Dead Angel

Dead angel lying on the road, overrun by pain
The sight of the unknown, drives the world insane.

I wish I was that angel, left there to die
I wish my wings were fixed, fixed so I could fly.

The dangers pass by quick, untouchable fear,
No smiles, dark eyes, a sweet tasting tear.

The blood runs out my arms, it's black and gold,
I can't do anything, my blood has gone cold.

My white gown is darkened, stains of fear and pain,
My face had so much expression, now I just looked plain.

Doesn't anyone care, that angels start to die,
By thousands, by millions, as the hours pass by.

I try to fly once more, the blood comes straight from Hell,
Even though I try my best, I never do well.

So I lie in the road, learn that angels die,
Even angels see the dark, even angels stop to fly.

One last breath, from the poisoned air,
Ruined by people, who think it's fair.

A name has been given, where we all go,
The place of dead angels, where you will find no halo.

I am that dead angel.

Janine Kessel (14)

TWINS

My mum is a twin
When she looks in the mirror
She sees a reflection of
Herself but really it's
Her twin who's identical.

This person is actually
The same as she is, the looks,
The hair everything is
The same except their
Lives are different.

These two people are
Different in many ways
But these twins sometimes feel
The same and think the same
At the same time.

It must be hard for
These two people being
The same when younger
Having to be dressed the
Same for many years.

Although the twins are
Now a lot older they
Still look the same in many ways
Although their personalities are
Different in many ways.

To this very day we
Still find it hard to tell
Them apart when they
Are not together, as
These twins will never change.

Sarah Giddings (14)

THE SEA

If I trust the sea
The sea will trust me
And everything will be brilliant
But if I don't trust the sea
The sea won't trust me and
Everything will be but pain.

The sea shines like a
Spark shimmering in my mother's eye,
And the waves break like white horses,
Galloping in a green-bluey field.

Every wave brings a mystical mist,
As the sand glistens beneath me,
The sea creatures shudder as a
Storm brews above and the sharks
Cackle with laughter.

If the wind begins to whistle,
The sea begins to roar,
And the helpless seashells
Cry out and shout for 'Help!'

The sea is full of things, many things
That either crawl, walk, swim or slither
They may hide, hunt or defend
They eat weed, coral, sea insects,
Other kinds of creatures even their
Own kind.

The sea can get angry or happy, even very sad,
The oceans and the sea show us this as the tide comes in
Either fierce, gentle or slow,
The sea is at its best when it's happy and gentle,
And when the sun makes it warm and calm!

Sarah Bird (14)

What A World Cup For The Cheerleaders

The day came
The 'Tastic Toros were excited,
Until they saw the Cool Clovers,
It was going to be a close competition
Even though winning was the Toros tradition.

The music started playing,
The leaders got in their places,
The cheer had started,
You should have seen the crowd's faces.

The boys were strong,
Girls flexible and light,
They all worked together,
And produced a routine.

The cheers were catchy,
The leaders were great,
The routine better,
The teams prayed for their fate.

The judges looked very happy
But had to make a hard decision
Their day had gone well
No injuries or twisted ankles.

It was presentation time
The judges had to tell the leaders who had won
They had two cups for first and second
The Toros came second with a small cup
The Clovers first with a large cup that was the World Cup.

They celebrated a lot
The Toros did too, they were glad to get
To the final in the Cheerleader World Cup.

Joanne Douglass (13)

Lament Of A Teenage Girl

Does my hair look alright?
Is the ponytail too tight?
Should I put it in a plait
Or will it make my face look fat?

Are my nails at all chipped?
Are they broken, need a clip?
Is the varnish too bright pink
Or too dull, what do you think?

Is my lipstick smudged or rubbed?
Do my teeth need to be scrubbed?
Is my mouth okay this red
Or does it make my teeth look dead?

Has my mascara run?
(This really is no fun!)
Is it too dark for me?
Should I wear this or Miss Sporty?

Does my top come down too low?
Is anything on show?
Does the colour suit my skin?
Does it make me look too thin?

Are my trousers the right style?
(They've not been worn for a while!)
Do they make my bum look right?
Are they too baggy or too tight?

Am I OK to go out?
No one will point and shout?
Please tell me I'm okay,
To go to school today!

Alice Harrison (13)

My Best Mate

She's absolutely crazy,
She's wacky and she's mad,
She's sometimes a bit lazy
But never ever sad!

She's funny and she's smart,
She's trendy and she's tall,
She's very good at art
But hang on, that's not all.

She loves to dance about,
She's always got a date,
She likes to scream and shout,
And she's my great best mate.

Her name is Steffi B
Who likes to play with toys
She sometimes calls me Lea,
Ideal for all the boys!

So wouldn't you agree,
I've got the best, best mate
Whose name is Steffi B
Who I will never ever hate!

Lianne Williams (13)

Love

Love is an emotion
Full of passion and obsession
There may be jealousy and confusion
But love is for everyone.

Alaina Wheeler (13)

Summer Holidays

I just can't wait until I'm out of school
I'll be out and about splashing in the pool.
Singing and dancing in the sun
Playing with my mates is so much fun.
Shopping sprees and lots of bags,
Buying all the latest mags.
At the seaside with my mum
Donkey rides hurt my bum!
Going to the funfair with my sis,
It's a really big event that you just can't miss.

It's getting a bit boring now, nothing much to do
My mum's doing my head in, my dad is too!
Three weeks left now, my friends are all away
Can't stand being bored no more, especially today.
Getting very stressed now, music on full blast,
Broke my arm on the swing and now it's in a cast.
I feel like the world's against me, what have I done wrong?
How much time is left now, I hope it's not too long!

Tara McKitton (13)

One Hundred Years

E verlasting pride flows over Merseyside
V ictorious once again, the away team scores a goal
E verton forever, wherever they shall go
R eckless challenge, that's another player down
T erraces arise; Everton pull one back
O ne hundred years in top flight football, it's the centenary year
N on-stop action, throughout the second half.

F ootball fever ignites the Goodison crowd
C ampbell scores in stoppage time, Everton don't go down!

Nigel Hughes (15)

My Friend Fiona

I've got a friend called Fiona
She's really a friend indeed
She's funny, she's cheerful
And don't forget
She's really quite insane.

I've been friends with Fiona
For nearly seven years now
And that's a long time for me
So every time I'm down in the dumps
She comes and checks me up.

She tells me funny things
And I can't help but laugh,
She's ever so funny
I end up with a sore tummy
I guess that's just Fiona.

Fiona's my best friend
And I guess she always will be
I will never ever fall out with her
Because Fiona's my best friend forever!

I've never had a friend like Fiona
Maybe she's special;
Well I tell you now,
Without a row
She is certainly
Special to me.

Emma McKellar

TEENAGE LIFE

I have a dream
Strange as it may seem
Things are going to look up
Don't drink from the Devil's cup.

Fashion and make-up are all the range
But through years it can always change
Through school life homework is such a bore
But it will help for life's problems and sores.

I find different things to do
So the family does too
Don't expect too much too soon
Just relax, sit and watch the night moon.

Pop music is cool
But don't play it in school
All music is great
But classical is not, mate.

My dream is to become a singer
But that's what many girls linger
If I can't sing then maybe a nursery teacher
Which will be fun but I wouldn't be a preacher.

So that's all from me
So let's wait and see
What will happen in later years
That won't bring me tears.

Claire Baseley (14)

A Troubled Mind

This is the story of a troubled mind
He lived in a semi-detached,
Which helped him feel unlatched,
As he grew up in a family who were kind!

His name was Michael Hart
There were some shouts
And incredible doubts
Then his family began to part.

The boy couldn't sleep at nights
He never emitted a single yawn,
As he waited quietly until the dawn
This caused the boy to get into fights.

He had a problem with authority
That got him into trouble.
But to make it double,
He was part of the minority!

But his problem is plain to see
His family love him
His friends like him
For Michael Hart is me!

Michael Hart (13)

Macbeth's Spell

Be you peasant or be you royal
A spell for Macbeth that shall make a king loyal.
Ear of cat to make you crafty,
Lion's toenail to make you majesty.
Owl's feathers to make you wise
And a mixture of herbs so you'll tell no lies

All these things in my magic potion
Will guarantee satisfaction.
Boil it up and swirl it around
A few small sips and you're bound to astound.
Now go forth and rule this land,
Face it with courage and an iron hand.

John Paddon (13)

GHOST

The haunted house stands tall and high
Just below the stormy sky.
Windows cracked and door ajar,
Dead flowers and a rusty car.

My heart's pounding and my breath's gone cold,
I take a step forward, I must be bold.
I open the door and hold my breath,
The hall is eerie, I can sense death.

Cobwebs choke the ceiling and stairs,
Pictures of people, horses and bears.
A door on the left, a door on the right,
Or shall I go upstairs towards the light?

Along the corridor, all musty and dark,
Stop and listen! A voice or a bark?
My legs shake and so does my spine,
I hear a floorboard creak and a door whine.

The light gets brighter as I enter the top floor,
I count to ten before I open the door.
I freeze in the doorway and so does the child,
Then it screams 'Ghost' and runs out wild.

Vanessa Hayter (14)

THE WIND

The wind, he is like an angel from Heaven
On a hot summer's day
Other times he is temperamental, you never now exactly what to expect
Some days he's like a gentle old man
Light and breezy,
Frail and floppy,
Lonely and tiresome.

But when he is upset he transforms
Into a raging bull
Strong and determined,
Angry and agitated,
A fearless fighter.

Although some days the wind in effect
Is like a Minotaur
A Greek myth,
Half man, half bull,
A mixture of strengths,
The good and the bad.

A mixture of expectations.

Amy Milnthorp (13)

KIND/CRUEL

My sister is stubborn,
My brother is cruel
And sometimes they drive me mad.
Maybe they're kind,
Maybe they're sad
But they know how to charge me up.
My brother bites,
My sister fights

They're both as cruel as each other.
Sometimes they give me sweets,
Sometimes they give me beats,
They make me happy,
They make me sad,
They make me angry,
They make me laugh.

Cecil Goodridge (13)

MY ROOM

I walk into my room
And what do I see
A beautiful, big dolphin
Looking back at me.

My room is blue
And I love it so true
Come and visit
If you want to.

My friends and I
Play in my room
Until we can see
The bright, yellow moon.

When they go home
I sit alone
Thinking of my dreams
And what could they mean.

Then in my bed
I go to sleep
Thinking of tomorrow
Will it bring joy
Or will it bring sorrow?

Naomi Magee (13)

That's Life

Life: how do we survive without TV? We ask our parents.
We just read books, played, sewed and talked.
Hanging with my mates watching TV.

Life: boys, do we really like them that much? We ask ourselves.
So many cute boys but so little time.
Hanging with my mates, boy-watching.

Life: 'Is your room tidy?' Mum asks me.
It's tidy to me but to Mum it's messy.
Hanging with my mates, listening to music.

Life: how can you not like shopping? Girls ask.
If only there was an unlimited amount of cash.
Hanging with my mates, window-shopping.

Life: who doesn't hate homework? Every teen asks.
If only there was a machine that did it for you.
Hanging with my mates, relaxing at last.

Holly Black (13)

My Holiday

I went to Spain
To get away from the rain
But when I was there
I got an awful scare.

I saw the flashes of lightning
And the sound of the thunder was frightening
The rain it poured down
Through the streets and the town.

But soon it was sunny again
And I forgot about the rain.
One night I realised my favourite pop band, Blue
Had been at the same restaurant as me too.

It was time to pack my bags
And hope I wouldn't have jet lag.
When I got home I had a good tan
And everyone asked did I get a Spanish man.

Charlene Seffen (15)

THE MIND

A hand that always helps,
An ear that always listens,
A friend that never judges,
A memory that glistens.

A light at the end of a tunnel
A piece of hope that lets you dream
With its movement it keeps you here on this Earth,
It's a trigger to wipe the slate clean.

An active little robot
That lives inside your head
A troublesome strong-minded fighter,
That without it I'm afraid we'd be dead.

It isn't a mum or a sister
It isn't that hard to find
It's much closer to home than you ever could roam
Yeah you guessed it, that lifeline's your mind.

Katie Larkin (13)

Hate and Love Are Just Two Words

Hate and love are just two words
But really they are rarely heard.
Someone says, 'I love you too.'
It's rarely meant and not for you.

For I have heard that mean, cold word
To me it isn't a bit absurd
It doesn't mean a thing to me
Apart from friends and family.

Maybe to someone it means true love
But I think it means what's said above,
For someone who really loves too
Is always there and cares for you.

But they were not there,
And now they're gone
And I'm the only lonely one.

I could just say I hate them too
But that is wrong and not so true.
Maybe this is a bit absurd,
But love and hate are just two words.

Alison Roberts (14)

Do We Care?

In our warm homes,
We seem so vain.
Whilst others are alone,
Weak and in pain.

But do we stop,
And say a prayer,
For the people who need us -
Do we care?

So should we pause,
And think about,
Those in famine,
Those in drought.

Next time you're eating,
Or chatting on the phone.
Think about how you could help,
People suffering on their own.

Michelle Tombs (13)

MIXED EMOTIONS ON LOSING SOMEONE

Obviously there's tears
And even fears.
Knowing we can't hold you
And tell you things we never told you.

Maybe there's some anger,
Thinking about how you've left us
Or even it's the fact that it hurts,
Not hearing or seeing you.

But then there's the cheer,
Wiping away the lingering tears,
Remembering moments spent with you,
Seeing things from a different view.

Then we realise,
We can never part,
As you will live on and on
In the depths of our heart.

Natalie Kent (14)

SHOULD WE WORK?

Teachers try to teach,
But only half the class are listening
We don't see the point.

Us teens would prefer to be listening to music
Going out to town or surfing the net.
For some,
It's sex, drugs and rock 'n' roll
Not
Work, lessons or exams.

Parents try to tell us
That we'll need qualifications one day
But right now we don't see the point.

Why do homework?
When you could
Hang out with friends or go shopping;
They say it's fun to skive.

We live for the present
When perhaps we should be living for the future
Is it better to enjoy life now or enjoy life later?
I don't know
But perhaps we should find a balance.

Luke Barbanneau (14)

SHOPPING

Spending money is so much fun
Buying gifts for everyone.
Trying on dresses, tops and shoes
It's so difficult for me to choose.
Searching shops with my best friend

Indecision drives her round the bend.
Sitting down to have a drink
What to buy next, we must think.
After all that shopping our day comes to an end
We return to our homes, me and my friend.

Julie Gill (13)

Life

Life is like a biscuit
You take one bite and then you decide what you do with the rest
You can play with it wisely or be eager and finish it in one go.

Life is like a park
When you enter you only have a limit of time until your fun is over
Now, you can use the time sensibly or waste it and give up.

Life is like a story
It has a beginning and an end, but you never know what will
happen in-between
The way you go about it is all up to you.

Life is like a piece of paper
There are so many things that you can do with it, you'll lose count
Don't rush to explore, good things come to those who wait.

Life is like a road
Everybody begins at the same place but it's up to you where you finish
There are many ways to go about life.

Life is like life
It only comes around once so use the time wisely
Well,
It is your life!

Candace Bertram (13)

SCHOOL'S OUT FOR SUMMER

Friday afternoon and the school bell rings
I already can't remember a thing.
We all rush to the bus park
Not caring about our marks.
Oh no, I see my form teacher,
He acts like some kind of a preacher.
My bus arrives so I get on,
I turn and see the bus park's gone!
We are all shouting on the bus,
Some people really make a fuss.
The bus driver, he's getting cross,
Like we would ever give a toss!
The bus pulls into my village,
I get off first, what a privilege.
I am getting tired on my walk home,
I do not have to read another tome.
I arrive home at long last,
That school year is in the past.
Sit down and turn on the television
EastEnders or Friends? A hard decision.
My holiday will be great,
That is no mistake.

Kirsty McKenzie (13)

AMBITIONS

I used to want to be a singer
Singing high and low and loud
Or at least to be something that makes me stand out from the crowd.
Maybe an artist with lots of French flair
(Well at least I tried but I didn't quite get there!)
Or maybe an actress to act on the big screen
(I thought about that a bit but it wasn't quite my scene!)

Well I can act a bit
But my drawings don't fit.
I sing around my house a lot
But I'm not going to try to be something I'm not
And then I realised that my ambition should be
To be something that's as individual as me.

Rachael Boddy (13)

THIN LIVING

Slinking down the catwalk
Bones jutting out
Bodies sucked in
Face moulded, a plastic glare.

Huddled over TV
Watching
Guiltily glancing at the empty crisp bag
Lying on the floor.

Film stars promenading down red carpets
Eyes flashing with tired lust
Paper skin stretched over bone collections.

Adverts shrieking from bus stops
Stick women
Preening wispy bodies.

I can't be like that
Glancing at the bag of crisps
But I can.

'Girl dies after fifty-three day starvation ordeal'
And they wonder why.

Geraldine Wood (14)

Parents

Parents are who you look up to
They tell you what you shouldn't do.
When you are young they help you
Parents are great, don't you think?

When you're feeling sick and ill,
They will look after you whatever the bill.
They are always there
Parents are great, don't you think?

When you're excited and going out places,
Parents take joy from the look on your faces
Parents are great, don't you think?

When you're in trouble and you know you've been bad,
It just makes your parents feel sad.
Always supportive,
Ready to live
Parents are great, don't you think?

Amy Sibley (13)

Darkness

Encased deep within this oblivion,
Chanting in my mind
I hold the anxiety within myself,
Scared of what I may find.

Dreaming of what could be waiting,
Wondering, what could be beyond
Yet within each breathe I keep falling,
As the darkness pulls me along.

Images flow from all angles,
I slowly open my eyes
My mind begins to conjure,
What it is that I want to find.

The secrets of night keep unfolding,
And I plunge deeper into my dreams.
The mystical time of the twilight,
Where nothing is as it seems.

Madiha Hameed (15)

LIFE

It's so hard to be a girl
Worrying about something new every day
Whether it be clothes, boys or make-up
Our insecurities never go away.

It's so easy to be a girl,
To chat to your friends each day,
To have your girlie chats with them,
But still be different in your own way.

It's so hard to be a teenager,
To try and want to fit in,
When you have a bad haircut,
And low self-esteem.

It's so easy to be a teenager,
To get the best you can,
To have your whole life ahead of you,
And find the perfect man!

Sarah McKibbin (13)

TEENAGERS

We are the best
So don't mess with me
Baggy trousers, down to
Our shoes, it's the fashion.
Loud music, walkmans and MP3 players,
So who cares? Not I
Deaf, dumb and blind
To all around.
Nokia to Samsung
Which ring tone? Msgs galore!
Parents nagging,
'Do this, do that.'
'Where are you going?'
'What time you back?'
'You're going out like that?'
Oh my, not my teenager
What do I care?
'It's the fashion' we cry
'Were you ever young?'
Off we go
Not a care in the world
What do they know?
They are only parents.

Lucy Tucker (13)

MY ONE TRUE FRIEND

My friend is like oxygen, I can't live without her,
She helps me when I'm stuck, she catches me when I fall
If life is not treating me right, she'll be there for me to make me smile.

She does not envy me for what I have, instead she chooses to admire,
She puts me before herself,
She watches over me, like my guardian angel.

She'll be here, when I need her,
She's so genuine and kind
My one true friend, we'll be together forever,
Always side by side.

Sarah Faust (13)

I'M SORRY

I'm so sorry for all the things I did to you.
I'm sorry for the way I spoke to you.
When you walked out of the door
My first reaction was to fall on the floor.
My head in my hands with tears down my face
I couldn't stop thinking about this disgrace.

I'm sorry I never told you
I thought you already knew
I'm sorry for what I said to you.

I never knew how you felt about me
I guess that's why it's only just come to me.
If only you could see how much you mean to me
I'm sorry, I'm sorry about this, I just wanted one last kiss.

I'm sorry I never told you
I thought you already knew
I'm sorry for what I said to you.

You walked out of the door and never walked back
Oh baby please come back.

I'm sorry I never told you this
I thought you already knew
That I love you.

Aby Chapman (15)

THE FIRST TEENAGE YEAR

When you're thirteen you should start to have fun,
As your teenage years have just begun.
You start to wear make-up and follow the trends
You like nothing more than to hang out with friends.

The downsides are bad, to avoid them is tricky
Your hair gets all greasy, the roots get quite sticky.
You wake up each morning with a brand new spot,
It's sometimes so bad you could play dot-to-dot.

The good parts are great so don't try to hide them
You become fond of boys when last year you despised them.
But then there are the mood swings, you get really mad,
You start to rebel, from angelic to bad.

You get masses of homework, your school is a bore
You wonder why you couldn't wait to go there before
But if you're a teenager get out and show it
Because the year will pass, before you know it.

Chelsea Faulkner (13)

THE MOON

We all live on the planet Earth
But I want to live on the moon
I could have all that peace to myself
I'm going to go there soon.

I'm going to build a spacecraft
Worthy of flight
Get the engines roaring
It's lift-off tonight.

I left the launch pad
And sped away
Towards the moon
Where I will stay.

I'm here now
Safe and sound
So if you will excuse me
I'm going to have a look around.

Kieran Hughes (13)

MIND OF A TEENAGER

Teenager in the morning
Waiting for the bus
No jacket and no breakfast
And nobody makes a fuss.

Teenager in the evening
Making toast for tea
Doesn't matter what he eats
There's no one there to see.

Teenager in the summer
Roaming far and wide,
An independent traveller
Just his shadow at his side.

Teenager, wise and wonderful
He's sharp and hard as a stone,
He knows he mustn't stumble when
He walks the world alone.

Thomas Sellers (15)

My Teenager Poem

I am now a teenager
To me this is something major,
I have to start making my own decisions
And take more part in writing competitions.
I am working really hard at school
So I can get a good job and look really cool
Sometimes I feel like bursting into tears,
This is where your friends come in.
They can be lovely little dears,
I love to go shopping,
And buy lots of clothes,
Basically, I love to buy loads and loads.
My hobbies are to sing and dance,
You need to grab your opportunity while you can,
It could be your last chance.
This may sound quite silly,
But in my opinion
Being a teenager is really . . . exciting!

Kiri Bain (13)

Fairy Lullaby

For Georgia Nicole - my baby sister.

When all the children are fast asleep
And midnight tolls its bell
Down amongst the flower beds
Is where the fairies dwell.

Out they fly to come and play
And laugh and scream and shout,
'We are the children of the night
Watch us jump and skip about!'

Then they clamber upon the ivy
And through the windows they do climb
To bless each child with fairy dreams
Until the church bells give their chime.

Then away our fairy friends
With pleasant thoughts and sleepyheads
Back to the place where no one knows
Down amongst the flower beds.

Rachel Bould (15)

Screwed Up Inside

My tears fall like rain
I can't stop the pain,
That I feel inside
So bad that I can't hide.

I want to get away
I've felt like this for days.

Then the lightning strikes
I'm back to reality,
If this carries on
I'll lose my sanity.

On my own again
Deserted by my friends,
My life is so messed up
Just want this all to stop.

I don't know what to do
But I've got to do it soon,
I can't take this any more
Why can't it be like before?

Richard Harvey (13)

STRESS

Stress! What is it?
Is it something you can't handle?
Is it something that gets on your nerves or
Is it just pressure of people?
Maybe you're feeling left out and lonely
It could be you just not pleased with yourself or your family and friends
And from all this you become depressed.
Then there are:-
Tablets,
Doctors,
Family,
Friends,
Strangers,
Fashion,
Homework,
Teachers,
And so much more
All this comes form just one five-lettered word *stress*.

Iqra Khan (13)

LONELINESS

L onely nights, I spend alone
O riginally it was with you
N o one thought we would last
E ven though that's in the past
L eaving you was hard to do,
I n my dreams, I think of you
N othing's left of what we had,
E mptiness, my mind's gone mad
S itting here I wonder now
S urely I'll find you again. Somehow.

Laura Whitehouse (15)

THE PILOT

We are on our way to bomb the base
On the way back there will be a big chase
Guns will fire and planes will soar
And from the ground you will hear a great roar.

As we approach the base everything is black
This is good for us because it's a surprise attack
But as we get nearer the spotlights come on
And with that some people chicken out and then they're gone.

But I am staying to fight, I will stand tall
That's if I don't get shot, it's a long fall
The first bombs go down and flashes can be seen
Then some wanna be heroes fly down, they seem a bit keen.

Then the captain shouts, 'You're going too fast!'
But it's too late, all you hear is a blast
We all swoop down and bomb, because we're being attacked
Now I can hear people being shot, this is their last act.

The main parts are destroyed and now it's the chase
Now it's all about the best and fastest flyers, so it's more of a race
You can see the bullets from the enemy planes
They whizz past so fast, it sounds like rattling chains.

I'm totally surrounded now and there's no way out
So all my friends and I can do is scream and shout
And then we get shot in the wing, so our plane starts to fall
I'm not sorry I'm going to die, because I know, I stood tall.

Kevin Kerridge (15)

War In The World Worries Me

It was the night before war,
He lived all alone,
In this one bedroom house made of plaster and stone.
I had knocked on the door with songs and cheers to give
And to see just who in this house did live.
I looked all about, it was a strange sight to see,
No light, no chairs, not one pot of tea.
No wood by the fire, just boots filled with sand,
On the wall hung pictures of far distant lands
With gold medals and badges, awards of all kinds
A sudden thought, shot through my mind.
This house was different, so empty and dreary
I'd found the house of a soldier, now I'd seen clearly
The soldier lay sleeping, silent, alone
Curled up on the stone floor in this one bedroom home.
His face was so gentle, the room getting colder
Not how I'd pictured a United States soldier.
Was this a hero who'd suffered and bled?
Curled up on a stone the floor for his bed.
I'd realised the families that I'd seen that night
Owed their lives to these soldiers who were willing to fight.
Soon round the world, children would play
And grown-ups would celebrate a bright, sunny day.
They all enjoyed freedom each month of each year
Because of the soldiers like the one lying here.
I couldn't help wonder how many lay alone
On a cold, icy flood, in a land far from home . . .

Gina Kakouri (13)

FRIENDS

When people hurt you or let you down
They are there to lift the frown.

When things don't go the way they're planned
They are there to lend a hand.

When life is hard at times of worry
They are there in a hurry.

When hope for the future seems far away
They are there throughout each day.

Who are they? You might ask
Friends to help with every task.

To share the troubles and dismay
To help make the sad things go away.

Loyalty, honesty, pure and true
These are qualities they look for in you.

So next time you see someone lonely in the street
Say, 'Hi,' you never know who you will meet.

Nicola Quinn (14)

TEENAGERS

We are teenagers from thirteen to nineteen,
We can do what we like when we like,
We eat fast food (chips and burgers),
We party most of the time,
We listen to loud music,
We drive our parents up the wall,
But we don't care because that is what teenagers are for.

Lynn Richardson (15)

The Accident

I saw it coming towards us,
Faster, faster and still faster.
Like a huge double decker bus
The brakes must have failed.
The headlights brighter and brighter still
The driver panicking
As he tries to turn the wheel.
Nothing we can do
Just sit and wait.
Sit and wait, good idea
But what if it's too late?
The big bang, the big crash
None of us moving at all
Unsure of each other's injures
Waiting for the ambulance call.
The ambulance arrives,
Paramedics running around,
Seeing our injuries
Then off to hospital bound.
Lying in the hospital bed
Attached to wires of all colours,
Blues, pinks, yellows and reds.
I lay and wonder. . .
Was it his or our fault?

Victoria Cottle (13)

Blue

Steps out of the shade
Over his shoulders are the pilot lights
Now the embraced talent of iron
Fused metal wept around his face, tears ran down.
The singeing sky that hurt him
Propeller blades that spin
Planting my shadow in the light
The heatwave that shocked burning pleasures in his night.
As death was dropped,
As burning blooms of cherry droplets, hit the fatal skin.
It leaves the print of your religion
A star, a yellow shape
As the scalds are not lost,
Your eternity around my finger,
A symbol of our love,
A tattered picture of you is all
To keep me through the night.
My tears are tears of debris
Molten people scream
A once majestic town of beauty,
A town of rubble now
As the pylon eels electrify my vanity
Now a mask of tinted iron
A hot white ore keeps me from you,
So I walk into the blue.

Andrew James (14)

Best Mates

Sometimes I am wrong
Sometimes I am right,
No matter what goes on we never, ever fight.
They're people I can turn to
Not only one but two,
Everybody else can see
Mates we are. Mates are we.
Even if I move away
We'll be mates all the way
Mates all day, mates all night,
Mates we are, who never fight.
Mates we are, mates are we
Mates, mates as you can see.

Chloe Jeffery (13)

It's Not Goodbye, It's Just See Ya Later

The one person we knew the best went away within a day
We questioned why, so young you went
And left the ones who love you most
Forever we'll remember the cherished moments
And wait for the day when we'll meet again.
Your two little angels suffer the most
Your mum, your wife and all our family.
Our hearts broke the night you went
But it's not goodbye
It's just see ya later.

Keshina Bouri (13)

DOVES

What is there in a childhood dream,
When life looks complete without a seam?
But when that dream is a love,
It flies away like a poor, white dove.

Lonely and willowed, the seasons pass,
The years rush in, concealed en mass,
Life is short, time is fast,
Any time we have, it rushes past.

There are four doves in the world today,
Faith, hope, trust and charity.
But in the wars, how many doves have been slain?
As trust is often the one betrayen.

So heed my call, a cry for help,
From the smallest squeak to the loudest yelp,
Let us save society, crumbling mankind
And leave our treacherous past behind.

Terri Ferguson (15)

I WANT . . .

I want to be like Britney, all thin and sexy like her.
I want a guy like Gareth to fancy me not her.
I want to have a house that's full of loads of stuff.
I want to have a body that will always look good.
I want to be a movie star with money here and there.
I want to have a perfect life but I know that isn't fair.

Kate Sales (14)

LOST BUT NOT FOUND

You're lost, bemused,
Dazed and confused;
It's what your life only seems to involve.
You try to think and focus your mind,
But you know it's not going to work
You just can't stop crying your heart out,
Crying out your heart, feelings and emotions to no one but yourself.
You call for help;
You keep calling till you can call no more,
But -
Nothing.
No one.
You are a prisoner inside yourself.
It's your life and only you can
Deal with it;
The show must go on.

Daniel Christopher (14)

WHAT COULD I SAY?

One cold night I would lie in my bed
Wondering what I had done and said.
Rows over here, rows over there
So anxious what to say I would just have to stare!
Fighting all night, fighting all day
Even fighting when I was asked out to play!
We would not talk for a long, long time
Over silly things like, 'Get off it's mine!'
After fighting I would feel very depressed,
But also glad to get it off my chest!

Fiona Rasch (13)

My World

Let us live in Toyland with Noddy and Big Ears where there is no hurt
No regret and no pain
It seems to me that it's all just playing,
Where the sun shines brightly every day,
And where the families are perfect in every way.

Where the children are free to do as they wish,
While eating their dinner they could play go fish,
Where they could eat their meals without using a knife,
And best of all they have their own social life.

I'd like to go there or somewhere similar - just to get away,
Of course not forever only for the day,
To get away from the people those irritate me the most,
Especially the people who like to boast,
Or the people who think they are so hard and tough,
Because their parents and them all live rough.

But the days would be long and we would be out of place
I get sick of Noddy and end up shouting, 'Get out of my face,'
I would miss my home and my mum too
But I wouldn't miss the work that I usually have to do.

But I suppose bad stuff happens to us all and we can't just go around it,
Everyone has got some luck and I guess I just haven't found it
So I'll keep on looking with a smile on my face
And I'll keep reminding myself it wouldn't be right for me to be in any other place.

Kylie Thomson (14)